THE AMAZONS

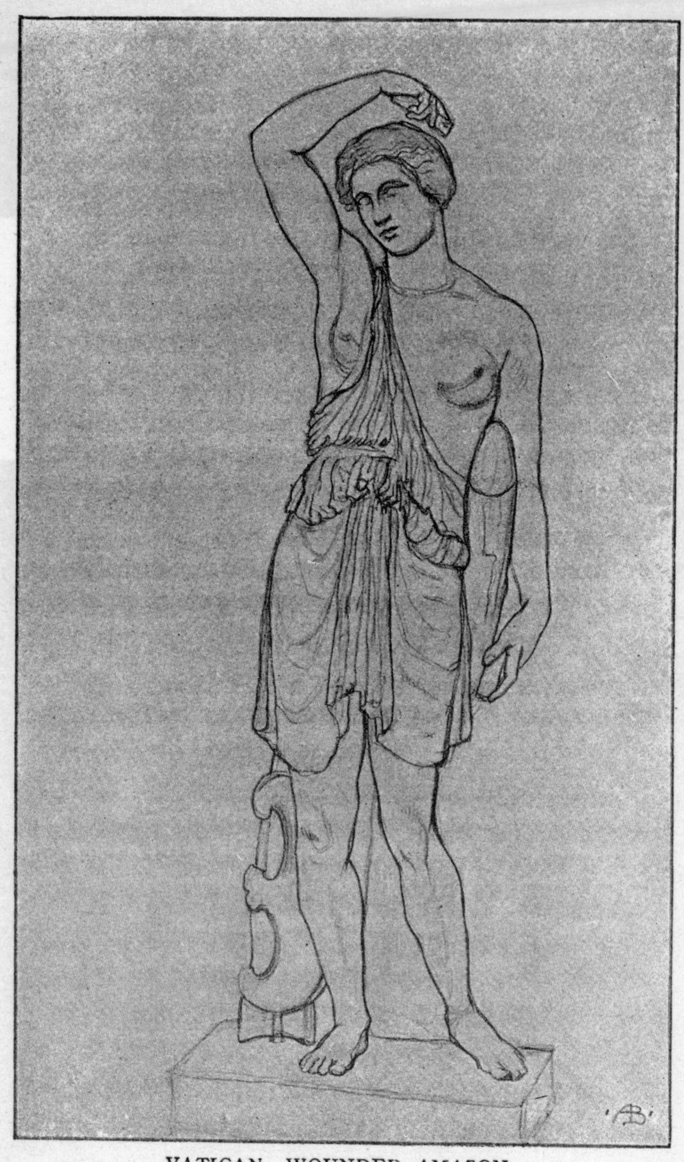

VATICAN, WOUNDED AMAZON.
ATTRIBUTED TO PHEIDIAS.

Frontispiece.]

THE AMAZONS

GUY CADOGAN ROTHERY

The Amazons

First published in 1910 by Francis Griffiths, London

This edition published in 1995 by Senate, an imprint of Studio Editions Ltd, Princess House, 50 Eastcastle Street, London W1N 7AP, England

ISBN 1 85958 180 3
Printed and bound in Guernsey by
The Guernsey Press Co. Ltd

CONTENTS

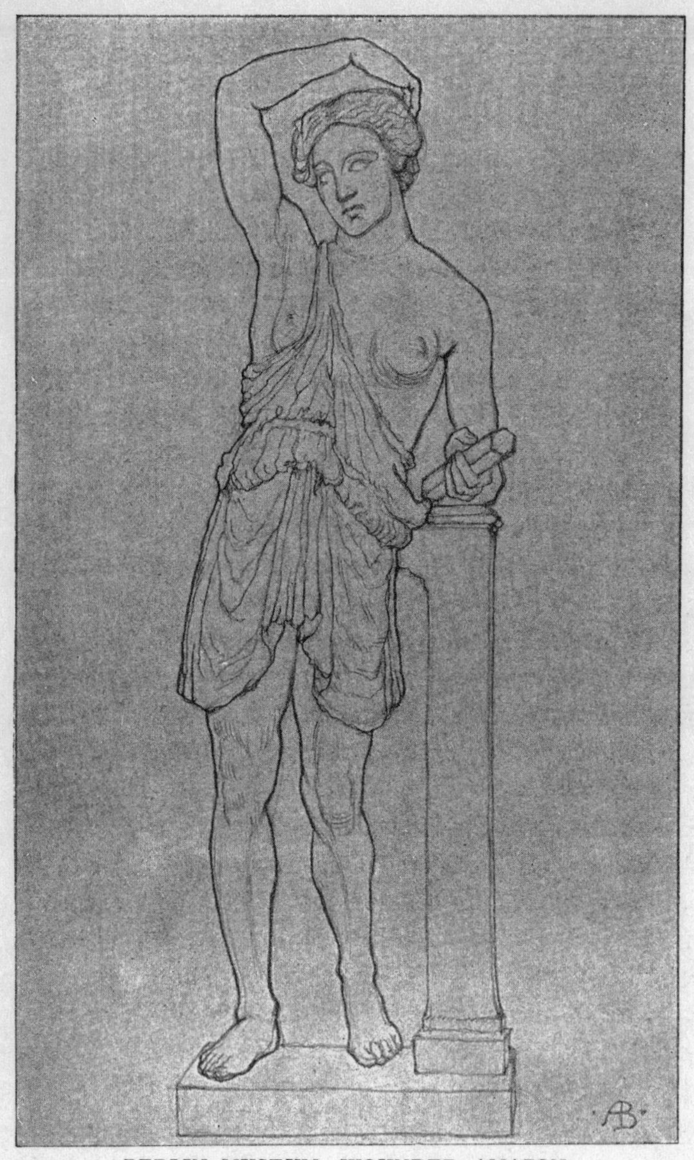

BERLIN MUSEUM, WOUNDED AMAZON.
ATTRIBUTED TO POLYCLETUS, SCULPTOR.

Facing page 1.]

THE AMAZONS

CHAPTER I

Introductory

Never, perhaps, has the alchemy of Greek genius been more potent than in the matter of the Amazonian myth. It has bestowed a charm on the whole amázing story which has been most prolific in its results; but, unfortunately, by tending to confine it to the narrow vistas of poetry, the intensely interesting psychological aspect has been somewhat obscured. Yet to us the chief value of this myth is due rather to the insight it affords into the mental workings of primitive races, the attitude of man towards that which he dreads but does not fully comprehend, than to the influence of Hellenic art and literature, fruitful in beautiful and humanising manifestations though that influence has been. The Greek spirit, indeed, working upon a crude collection of stories, took the sting out of the lessons they should have taught. For, as we shall endeavour to show, the message of the myth to a people struggling towards a higher civilisation to beware of barbarians and their ways, was softened to an attitude of admiration before physical beauty and courage, and a tender pity for woman, fomenter of strife though she might be.

We may unhesitatingly sweep away the story of the unnatural state about which so many Greek poets and historians entertain us. But while relegating the Amazonian state to the realms of imagination, we must recognise the Amazon herself as a not insignificant historic fact—a fact, indeed, of sufficient moment to have peopled a whole world of fiction, real enough to its original creators, and whose force is hardly spent even now.

Etymology will not help us much, though it has been relied upon by controversialists. Any argument founded on the descriptive nature of the word, or on its somewhat suspicious many-sidedness, must prove a double-edged weapon, as likely to injure the wielder as his opponent. Besides the obvious "breastless" (*a-mazon*) and "moon" (*maza*), we are offered a choice of a variety of interpretations conveying to us such meanings as "vestals," "girdle-bearers," and other synonyms, also "game eaters" and "eaters of strong foods." But after all the word is hybrid Greek, not a native name, and may be classed as a nickname, itself much younger than the supposed state; and then, naturally, it would be as comprehensively descriptive as the ingenuity of man could devise. We may, therefore, leave the etymologists to the labyrinthine twistings of their own wordy warfare.

The tale begins rationally enough with the perfectly familiar incident in the life-history of so many nations, the expulsion of a surplus growth of population and its emigration to new fields. In this case we have reference to a cabal against two youthful Scythian princes, who, being ordered into exile, carry with them a whole horde of followers—men, women, and children. There is the story of their settling down, of their casting off of the old Scythian simplicity before a growing desire for riches, which leads to conquest and ultimately to their undoing—the men being mostly massacred by their enraged neighbours. Then comes the extraordinary violent rage of the widows and orphans, first against the slayers of their husbands and fathers, and later against men in general, this aversion bringing about the founding of a state that is to be manless, the women throwing aside their girdles, that priceless symbol of the unmarried, only for a brief spell in the spring-time, when by commerce with their male neighbours means should be taken to guard against the extinction of the race.

That such a myth should have sprung to life and gained credence is not difficult to understand. To the inhabitants of the Archipelago and Magna Grecia, no matter whence they originated, distant Asia and the regions to the north-east of the Black Sea and round about the Caspian were lands of peril shrouded in mystery, out of which fierce hordes swept down bent on rapine and conquest. Beyond the fringe of the nearer Mediterranean coast there were worlds of darkness, peopled by the fertile Greek mind with many unnatural but by no means illogically conceived monsters; for the makers of the myths had hardly emerged from the influence of animistic interpretation of nature. All phenomena were explainable in the terms of human emotions, and man acknowledged himself the relation, and not always the superior relation, of the beasts of the field, nay, even of the stocks and stones. To such men, nomadic tribes from the sandy Asian wastes bursting out of clouds of dust on their fleet horses to pillage and slaughter and then as swiftly pass away, had suggested the Centaur myth, the man-horses lying behind the woods ready to swoop down upon the unwary. The aborigines of forest districts, whose attacks were as dangerous and unexpected as that of the wild boar and wild goat, naturally suggested the satyrs. That yet older terror, the herds of wild buffaloes with their irresistible onrush and indomitable fierceness, had given birth to the superhumanly cunning winged man-bulls of Assyria. Successive waves of invasion rolling seaward from the north-east made utter Scythia a constant source of danger, and when the reflux waves carried the over-swollen coast population north-eastward, they entered an inhospitable country, where pitchy lakes and unctuous soil belched forth fire, smoke, and steam, an ominous presage of what might be expected beyond. Towering above stood a further barrier of rugged black mountains, inhabited by a race of savage warriors whose very women fought with all the ferocity of lionesses. This ever-menacing danger, with dim recollections of an out-worn stage of development, when a matriarchal polity prevailed, and the nearer, more ghastly remembrance of the worship of cruel, sensual Astarte, that moon huntress goddess who came out of the Far East smeared with human gore, surrounded by her women priests, evolved in the brains of men whose thoughts were prone to take the dramatic form the idea of a truly monstrous state, the very existence of which was a perpetual threat against humanity. Indeed, the Amazonian state, with its population of women warriors, ruled by a queen who banished all men save a few crippled slaves, and banded together with the express purpose of making war upon mankind, perfectly symbolised the peril that Greece had to face. For the myth told not merely of war, but of unnatural war, war which if successful foredoomed family and civic life.

It is symbolic however we look upon it. A noteworthy fact is that certain legends made the Amazons worshippers of Artemis, while others declared them to be deadly enemies of that goddess and her followers. In art we find Amazons wearing the crescent moon on their heads; possibly, too, the triple-towered crown; while their shields were either crescent-shaped or round—these, with their spears and bows and arrows, are the emblems of the moon huntress goddess, both in the guise of savage Astarte and of her Hellenised, humanised counterpart, Artemis. It would be natural for a state whose people lived on the spoils of sport and warfare, who looked upon the sacrifice of male infants as a duty, who drank out of human skulls and were suspected of cannibalism, to worship Astarte, whose early history reeked of blood and was punctuated by mutilation, a deity who symbolised a stage of society when the hunting of wild beasts was of supreme importance. The apparent conflict between the various versions of the myth no doubt arose from a confusion brought about with the lapse of time between the two aspects of this goddess. In the early forms of the legend it would be quite in accordance with their general trend to associate the warrior women with a female deity who, at all events in the degenerate days of her cult in Asia Minor, represented lust *in excelsis.* And here, it is likely enough, the myth was founded on solid fact, for it is well-nigh certain that the savage horde from Scythia paid homage to some prototype of Astarte. Her worship is undoubtedly of Eastern origin; this being so, one more reason would be added for the Greeks looking with mingled anxiety and abhorrence to the north-east. Among the several great cities of antiquity which were said to have been founded by queens leading successive swarms from the great parent hive of the Amazonian state was Ephesus. We know that its celebrated Temple to Diana (Artemis) was attended by eunuch priests and probably contained statues of Amazons due to the chisels of the foremost of Grecian sculptors. Though her servants cried aloud, "Great is Diana of the Ephesians," she was really a mild version of Astarte, tamed by the influence of Greek art and thought. Another significant fact is that in its earlier forms the myths of the Amazons and gryphons are represented as implacable enemies, and even in quite late art they are jumbled up with the wars of the centaurs and the gigantomachia, which points to the realms of fancy.

All this, of course, does not do away with the historic fact that out of those dark regions warrior women came, now as leaders, at other times in bands—both as camp-followers and in the fighting ranks. The phenomena, indeed, can hardly be said to be peculiar to any age or clime. Our own island history records the valour of Boadicea, queen of the Iceni, her sudden tempestuous appearance, leading in the slaughter of the Roman legionaries, the sacking of Roman camps and cities, and noble in her reverses. History and art tell us that the women of Germania and Gaul fought against the Romans. And such incidents repeat themselves again and again. In 1792 the French Revolution brought forth an Amazonian brigade, and it is not without interest to note in passing that a worthy French historian had years before claimed that the Franks were direct descendants of the Sarmatian Amazons. The eighteenth-century brigade comprised the gross dames de la Halle and the women of the Faubourg St. Antoine, who, their blood aflame with the lust of killing, decked themselves out, with some dim thought of classic times (that heroic age which fired the thought of a whole revolutionary generation), in short petticoats, red Phrygian caps, and carried most business-like pikes. Plutarch tells us of the valiant women of Argos who defended their city against the Spartans so well that they were allowed to dedicate a statue to Mars, and the women were thenceforth permitted to wear false beards on their nuptial day.

But as regards fighting, have we not that far more piquant incident of Thalestris appearing before Alexander as he was marching through Parthia, fresh from the conquest of Persia and the defeat of the Scythians? That a queen leading an army with a legion of women warriors did come to offer homage there is much reason to think possible, though the title "Queen of the Amazons" may be put down as a later embroidery of Greek historians. Plutarch, it is true, treats the whole story as a fiction, and quotes Lysimachus and Alexander himself in support of his contention. Against this we have circumstantial accounts of the invasion of Persia in the time of Cyrus by "barbarians" led by women. Rumours of warrior women are very persistent in further Asia, and the tradition culminates in the comic-opera squadron of 150 Amazons enrolled under Ranjeet Singh of Lahore. In the Caucasus travellers reported the existence of bands of fighting women down to comparatively recent times, but they were part of the community, not representatives of a female state. The fashion spread westward, for we find Amazonian bands in Bohemia during the eighth century, and we have tales of an attempt to establish a matriarchate among those turbulent people.

From Africa we have early tales of Amazons, partly, no doubt, founded on the real existence of great queens and their women guards, but largely coloured by the Greek myth. We have stories of Amazons to the south-east of Egypt and that other land of terrors, which Lady Lugard has so graphically described, a land to the south of the civilised portion, a country of the Nem-nems, or the Lem-lems, or the Rem-rems, or the Dem-dems, or the Gnem-gnems (for the savages always bore a repeat name, and do so down to these days), and those who wrote of them invariably added, "who eat men."

Curiously enough, Greek authors refer both to the African Amazons of the east and middle north, who are said to have overrun Asia, and also to a great Amazonian invasion coming from Ethiopia in the west. Some, indeed, would have us believe that these were descendants of the Scythian Amazons, who had wandered across the Mediterranean, passed through the Straits, and reached the Hesperides, whence they attacked Ethiopia, and, marching eastward, entered Egypt, crossed over to the Ionian Isles and Asia, to be finally overthrown by Hercules. It is a most curious story this eastward invasion, with its plausible account of an alliance with Horus, son of Isis, a sun goddess, consort and successor of that primeval moon and corn god and king, the great, all-pervading Osiris, and herself identified with human sacrifice and mutilation. Now, the history of Africa north of the equator shows that there had been persistent penetrations from the east by a people of Asiatic origin coming through Arabia and westward by Africanised Asiatics, who, finding penetration from the Mediterranean shores slow, appear to have overrun the Atlantic coast and pushed eastward to blend with Nile infiltration. Did the fighting women come with the invaders, then truly descendants of the Amazons in the sense that these dames of spear and buckler had fought for many centuries side by side with their trucculent men-kind? or did the civilised Egyptians and Berbers, advancing cautiously, ever struggling with the black bi-named eaters of men, find lands of armed maidens ready to dispute their way? If so, we have a spontaneous growth, later to be exaggerated by the declamatory Greeks. Certain it is that we have early evidence of fighting bands of African women, perhaps the most famous of which are the eunuch-tended Congo and Dahomeyan Royal Guards, then the less definitely authenticated matriarchal countries of women-fighters on the eastward side, but no credible accounts of a woman-governed, manless state.

That America should possess its Amazons, not only armed cap-à-pie, but ruling over a man-free state, was inevitable. The fifteenth-century European was dominated by the Greek spirit. He went West, not to discover a new world, but to find a short cut to India, with its boundless wealth and all its wonders and monsters, as recorded by the ancients. Dreams of the lost Atlantis, the superb island-continent, the home of the Elysian fields, which had formed in imagination a mysterious and golden bridge between Africa and India, was a constant obsession to them. It accounted so conveniently for many problems and for so many of their plausible theories. Consequently, it is quite natural that the early explorers from all countries, but more especially those who had come into closer contact with and had received an intellectual stimulus from Arabic civilisation, should have seen things with a distorted vision, the result of preconceived ideas, unfailing credulity, and an abundant superstition. It is not necessary to disbelieve Francisco de Orellana's account of his meeting opposition from bands of armed women on the banks of the Marañon, and it was quite in the order of things that he should rename that river the Amazon, and straightway call forth from the vasty deep of his own credulity a state which was the exact counterpart of the Scythian Amazonia. That he and numerous other of his contemporaries had to make warfare on armed women may be accepted as fact; that they may have formed corps or "tribes" by themselves is possible. Native tradition itself is busy with tales of great queens and women leaders. We know that there were women priests, and in certain stages of evolution the priest is a leader and warrior. The elaborate tales of travellers who followed in the footsteps of the conquistadors, however, are suspect, both on account of their too close resemblance to Asiatic myths and because of the absence of corroboration in detail.

Of the historic Amazon little need be said for the moment. Under stress, human nature is very much to-day what it was yesterday and will be to-morrow; and woman, being woman, under stress is very apt to exaggerate human passions. It would be idle and tedious to labour the point which myth and history illustrate so well.

On the Greek humanising spirit we may dwell somewhat more at length. No graven or fictile representation of an Amazon approximately coeval with even the latest true myth-monger has come down to us. All the sculptures and decorated pottery we have belong to a comparatively late date, when the original abhorrence which had conjured up the myth was passing away. Literature, however, gives us some idea of the primitive view.

We are told of a turbulent, bloodthirsty race, cannibalistic, addicted to human sacrifice in their religious observances, sworn to repudiate the natural order of society, living only to make war on their neighbours, implacable in their hatreds. We see them disdaining Greek culture, rebels to the Greek demigods, overrunning Africa like demented Argonauts in search of a lieing belt (for never had symbolism been more audaciously misapplied than by the Amazonian assumption of the virginal girdle), laying siege to Athens, and only restrained from sacking Minerva's sacred city by the arts of diplomacy. It is a long story of rapine and robbery. Yet, even so early as the Homeric cycle of songs, the humanising spirit was at work. Achilles, called away from his duties to the dead Patroclus to stem the Trojan onslaught, is galled into Olympic anger by the vituperative and slaughter-dealing Amazonian queen and her captains, who had come to the aid of Priam merely to vent their rage against the Greeks. But in the very moment of his triumph, when victorious he is about to despoil the fallen queen, he is arrested by her physical beauty, and, admiring her warrior prowess, is seized with remorse that his hand should have delivered the death-blow to a woman. That the woman deserved her death, that she goaded Achilles to act in self-defence, does not alter the horror of the situation; for man feels himself in the wrong, no matter what the provocation. The pathos of such a situation called forth the best endeavours of art. The incident was dealt with at length by Arctinus of Miletus in his poem "Æthiopia," that continuation of the "Iliad," which his countrymen placed so high. It is an attitude towards the Amazons that is almost invariably found in Greek art. We have representations of their warfare with the gryphons and barbarians, their defeat by Hercules, their victories and repulses before Athens. We have them in groups and as single figures, not assuredly ideal female forms, for, although splendidly developed, and even in the vigorous postures of hand-to-hand combat, on foot or horseback, always graceful, there is a subtle suggestion in form and mien that is not quite feminine. The faces are generally strong, beautiful in outline, often tender in expression. There is, in fact, no hint of the virago in anything that the Greek sculptors have left for us, but there is that hint that these women were not as other women were. This is strictly in accordance with later Greek conception of the Amazons as a splendid race of women, sternly suppressing natural inclinations in the interests of their community and ideals. The rendering of such sentiments by artists is quite noticeable when we consider these sculptors in comparison with other examples of the Greek idealisation of the female form, whether it is a simpering Venus, a proud Diana, a majestic Athene, or, to come down to commoner clay, a laughing maiden and dignified matron. Now, if we further contrast this delicate suggestion of a difference founded on a natural deduction from the supposed ideal of the Amazon state with the violent representations of duality of personality as shown in Oriental art,—for instance, in the Arddhanarishwara,—we can the more clearly realise the refining influence of the Hellenic spirit. We can but pause in admiration at the sublimity of feeling and wondrous skill with which this is conveyed to the spectator. Yet, story for story, the ethical value of the Oriental is often far superior to that of the Occidental. But in the one case the spirituality is hidden, the representation of a beautiful thought is gross; in the other, on the contrary, it is sublimed. We may carry the comparison still further by contrasting the story of the rhackshasis-inhabited Ceylon, or the island of El Wak-Wak (which comes to us from India through Arabic sources), with the myth of the island of Ææa, where Circe dwelt surrounded by lovely handmaidens and her tamed wild beasts, bent, apparently, on much the same work as the Eastern women of inveigling men and then sacrificing them; but how poetically the cruelty underlying the lesson is softened. In the one case there is crude, vehement symbolism; in the other, much tender humanity. It is partly owing to the latter characteristic that when the Greek artists show men as opponents there may often be traced an underlying feeling of unwillingness. They are fighting to the death, but without hatred, though, of course, there are exceptions — such, for instance, as the two equestrian figures shown on a terra-cotta fragment in the Towneley Collection, where we see a beardless Greek youth bending forward on his rearing horse to seize with the left hand an Amazon by the hair, bending her head violently backwards; and as she falls, he lifts his right arm to strike her with a short sword. And there are many fierce combats in the larger relief sculptures.

As a rule, however, the artists seem bent on so telling the tale to the world that they may the more clearly impress the lesson they drew from the legends and from the hard struggles of life—"The pity of it, the pity of it!"

In the minor forms of art, the numismatic and fictile branches, we are as a rule a good deal closer in spirit, though by no means always in period of production, to the older versions of the legends. Because, of course, generally speaking, it is more popular art, which appealed to the *oi-poloi*. As regards numismatics of Hellenised countries, those tokens on which the apologists have relied so much in making out their case for the historical existence of the state, there is much that is extremely doubtful, a large number of the figures supposed to represent Amazons really being the geniuses of cities. There is, in fact, little to be gathered from them in this connection, either on the historic or the art side. In the pottery there is often a good deal that is rough, both in modelling and painting, and also in the matter of emotional expression. The crudeness is unquestionably due to its being popular art rather than to its age, for we find in many of the pieces a tendency to complication in design; the Amazons and Greeks do not fight face to face, but twist and turn about in elaborate evolutions, and this is often accompanied by a piling on of detail, thus getting away from the primitive types. But this pottery decoration is almost certainly imitative if not directly copyistic, too frequently falling to conscious caricature of the noble forms. The legends, in any case, were favourite themes with the potters, who frequently show us the Amazons at their favourite trades of killing and maiming. The stories of Bellerophon, Hercules, Hippolyta, and Theseus are portrayed with endless variations, not without considerable vigour. A point to be noted is that in these paintings the Amazonian queens have the heads of Medusa on their round targets, though sometimes the gorgeion masks are seen on the Greek shields, betraying a certain confusion of ideas, or perhaps the different moral point of view of the artist. While the struggles are generally between the women and Greeks, we occasionally find Amazons assisting the Greeks in their fights against monsters, and the scenes between Achilles and Penthesilea are shown boldly and with some regard to sentiment. There is also a notable variation in the matter of costume, ranging from the short tunic or the chiton to the armour-clad female warriors with their Athenian helmets and crescent-shaped shields, and then to the Persian type of Amazon in close-fitting tunics and trousers, with Phrygian caps, which is often in startling contrast to the starkness of their adversaries.

Apart from the crudeness naturally associated with a large portion of this work, which was mainly mechanical, the designs being stamped on the clay over and over again, we find attempts to show both the fierceness and the physical beauty of the women.

When we come to consider the sculptures, even the earliest specimens extant, we must not forget that they belong to an age far removed from the myth-mongers, a full thousand years later than the

CAPITOL MUSEUM, WOUNDED AMAZON.

Facing page 16.]

legendary days of Amazonian strength and pride. In this branch almost always the scenes of Amazon combats—be the warriors triumphant in victory or imposing in death—appear to express the Achillean divine sorrow mingled with respect. We can see this even in what remains of the friezes from the Temple of Æsculapius now at the Central Museum, Athens, though these fragments of statuary represent wonderfully lifelike incidents of the fiercest fighting, where the artists have put forth their best efforts to make the spectators enter into the feeling of the veritable frenzy of energy which seems actually to be enacted before them. An Amazon wounded in the throat slips from the back of her fleeing horse; another, fallen to her knees, shows a magnificent head in the agony of death; while in the forefront an Amazon, very much mutilated, is shown astride of a rearing horse, holding her steed by a muscular grip on its panting flanks: she is lifting her right arm apparently to strike forward with her deadly spear. The head and greater part of the right arm are missing, but both breasts are indicated under the folds of the draperies. Every figure is instinct with the strenuousness of the battle, displaying the subtleness of the perfectly trained, combined with great beauty of outline. Much care is shown with the drapery. In the sculptures from the Temple of Apollo the Deliverer erected at Phigaleia in the Peloponnesus, and preserved at the British Museum, there is an equally wonderful gallery of figures of Amazons and Greeks in battle, those of the female warriors having an arresting charm both when exhibiting the vigour of the fighters and the exhaustion of the vanquished. There are in those worn but yet splendid marbles many touching incidents, as well as a good deal of hard fighting. The grouping is spirited, the figures being so arranged as to stand out boldly, giving full value to the moving representations of the hazards, hardships, and rush of battle. A wounded Amazon whose horse has stumbled, thus pitching her forward, has her right foot seized by a Greek intent on completing her downfall. Another mounted Amazon is dragged from her horse by the head. This pulling back of the head by the hair in order to upset the equilibrium or deliver a deadly thrust is shown in three or four other groups, witnessing the intensity of its struggle. On the other hand, the Achillean remorse is given prominence in several places, though on the opposite side. A wounded Greek is supported by an Amazon, who has her arm passed behind his shoulders as she leads him away from the strife; another kneels down to lift a wounded sister; and in a third instance a woman thrusts forward her arms to ward off the threatened stroke aimed by an Amazon against a fallen foe. It must be said that the chivalry appears to be all on the feminine side, but the point is that there is chivalry shown in a fair fight. The Greek artist has not attempted to belittle or defame the warrior women, whom he regards as foes worthy of Hellenic steel and who are to be respected. This temple was built by Iktinos, who was associated with Pheidias in the designing of the Parthenon, and from what Pliny says it is clear that leading Athenian sculptors were responsible for its embellishment, so here we have the true Greek feeling. In both these instances the costumes of the Amazons are quite primitive. The chiton is worn, stopping short well above the knee, caught at the waist by a girdle, and carried across the breast to be fastened over the left shoulder. The legs and feet are bare, a strap sometimes being shown over the right ankle to hold the spur. The helmet, when worn, is of the Minerva type. Great skill is displayed in managing the drapery, so that it shows off the fine bodily development and the exertion. Simplicity is the characteristic of all the accessaries, throwing into greater prominence the physical beauties. The sculptures, now also at the British Museum, from the tomb of Mausolus, Satrap of Caria, which his widow erected at Halicarnassus, belong to a somewhat later date, and, though inspired by the same feeling, show more licence and less refinement in treatment. There is a reminiscence of the older artists. The drapery is longer and ample; the chlamis, flowing from the shoulder, is added; but in the violence of action the figures are rather apt to be startlingly undraped. There are characteristic touches which take us back to the Scythian wilds: an Amazon fleeing on horseback has vaulted round, and, though astride, faces the pursuing enemies, against whom she aims a dart—the Parthian bolt. Here the strife is very pronounced and many of the actions fierce, but it is a fight among equals.

The two first groups belong to the supreme age of Greek art, when the influence of Pheidias, Polyclitus, and Praxiteles was at work. Of the great masters themselves we have no certain examples, though five celebrated marble statues of Amazons are almost indubitably copies of their original bronzes. All five have a strong family likeness. The Vatican Amazon has been attributed to Pheidias, and though in part badly restored, is a thing of priceless beauty. This youthful warrior has been recognised as a special type, differing not so much in general design but in treatment; unlike the others, she is not supposed to be wounded in her right side. She leans on her lance in the left hand; the right arm (which has been restored) is lifted above the head, the fingers lightly twined about the upper part of the lance. There can be little doubt that the hand should be grasping it, the whole poise of the figure showing that she is preparing to vault on to the back of her horse. The body shows vigour, though in actual repose prior to vaulting; the face is calm, and almost sweet in spite of the firmness of the outline. She wears a short chiton, caught up at the waist and fastened over the right shoulder, leaving part of the left thigh and the chest exposed. There is some sign of the *a-mazon* mutilation; otherwise, it is a model of youthful perfection, though in some respects it might be that of an Adonis. The Capitoline Amazon shows even more tenderness, while true femininity is cleverly avoided. The head, however, is said to belong to another statue. The wounded girl, in her short chiton, the right leg slightly bent back from the knee, must have been represented as leaning on her lance with her right hand (but this has been restored so as to

VIENNA, WOUNDED AMAZON

Facing page 21.]

show it uplifted above the head), the left hand drawing the drapery away from her wounded side. There is no sign of the *a-mazon* mutilation in this statue; the right breast is exposed, but the left is expressed, though covered by drapery. The Berlin wounded Amazon has her right arm lifted above her head, as though instinctively raised from the sword-thrust in her side. She leans with her left arm on a column, her left leg is drawn back, contracted by pain; but, clear as is the evidence of anguish, there is no contortion of limb or features. The chiton is quite short, and there is little drapery over the upper part of the body; but the folds, which are elaborate, are at once decorative and natural. This statue has been attributed to Polyclitus, but is probably more justly claimed to be a copy of the original bronze, which may, according to the delightful story, have been the one set up in the Temple of Diana at Ephesus. It will be remembered that, according to a never-too-probable occurrence reported by Pliny, Pheidias, Polyclitus, Cresilas, and Phradmon, all competed for the honour of providing the *ex veto* Amazon, each being asked to make his vote for the best work. Each placed his own statue first and that of Polyclitus second, virtually a majority verdict for the latter. Though this story of competition has a certain air of reasonableness about it (for, according to very ancient tradition, Ephesus, whether or not originally founded by the Scythian women warriors, had given them refuge when hard pressed during their retreat after their dash into Attica), all that we can deduct from it is that statues of Amazons were shown in the temple. At all events, this tale of emulation among Greek sculptors to honour Artemis in her more tender moods as the Succourer illustrates the humanising spirit of their art, and would go to explain the undoubtedly striking similarity to the general design of the above three Amazons and those of the Lansdowne and Vienna Collections. We are here, certainly, very far from the dreadful bloodthirsty woman of the primitive legend, or even from the boastful queen of the "Iliad."

The myth, forged in the dim past, when strife was dire and inevitable, had played its part. As outward pressure relaxed, and men became more enlightened, the story lost much of its grimness, but had not spent its power: the poet and artist made it their own, drawing from its grim details new meanings, refining its lessons to fit them for a happier stage of civilisation. And so they softened the story of Amazonian cruelty to serve their own ends, promoting the cult of the beautiful by holding up the splendid human figures, at once strong and graceful, to the emulation of maid and matron, and by calling for masculine admiration and pity.

CHAPTER II

The Amazons of Antiquity

Running through the works of early Greek writers we find a moving and circumstantial story of the rise and fall of a nation of women, who, having been deprived of their husbands, sons, and brothers through the fortunes of battle, and then persecuted by the cruelty of their enemies, took up arms to avenge their wrongs. Thus having tasted blood, these women, we are told, acquired an unappeasable longing for the lust of carnage, and spurred on by the exaltation of victory, they decided to forswear the rule of man and become their own mistresses. Banishing, or mutilating, the few males left in their midst, they set about laying the foundations of a state, and, either through the necessities of the case or a liking for the calling, adopted arms as a national career. This monstrous experiment succeeding, the boundaries of the state were, if we are to believe various writers, vastly extended, the fame of the women warriors flying swiftly before their advancing legions, carrying terror into distant countries. Occasional war alliances were then formed with neighbouring people, to enable far-off and hazardous expeditions to be undertaken with greater ease. The women swept west as far as Bohemia, and some say into Gaul, reached the Mediterranean, penetrated India with conquering Dionysius, invaded Northern Africa to make treaties with Horus, son of Osiris and Isis, attacked Attica, actually sat down before proud Athens and almost beat her to the dust, founded colonies in Europe and Asia Minor, and built many cities renowned in history. Here, indeed, was a theme to inspire poets with eloquence, to be dwelt upon, embroidered and otherwise ornamented with diverse fantastic details by chroniclers; to endow the brush of painters, the chisel of sculptors with a fine frenzy, which has left us sometimes quaintly grotesque but frequently loftily conceived works of art.

It is a curious tale this story of the Amazons, disturbingly elusive when the positive evidence of monuments or other contemporary records are inquired after: a tale full of contradictions and pitfalls for the unwary, yet in its main outline consistent enough. It is impossible to date the story, though many compute it to have commenced between 2500 and 1500 years before our era, and others much earlier, taking into account the far-off expeditions and their merging into the realms of mythology. At all events, in some nebulous period and in an equally cloud-obscured region, the distant lands north-east of the Caucasus barrier, a conspiracy arose among the Scythians against two of their princes, named, we are told, Hylinos and Scolopotos, with the result that the milder alternative of banishment was resorted to. The princes and their families, their followers and their families, their partisans and their families—a nation in miniature—were pushed over the borderland, and came rushing to the foot and up the slopes of the Caucasus like the swollen yellow flood of an overfull river. Naturally they slew and stole, settling down to fill places high and places low of the dispossessed. Then, as we might expect, came an uprising of the oppressed when least looked for, but an uprising so successful in its first deceptive appearance that the festering sore caused by the implanted strangers was well-nigh wiped off the face of the land. The slaughter of the Scythian men was terrific, and of a thoroughness characteristic of those good old times. But the women of the hardy race, inured to hardships by their tribe's recent experiences, retired fighting to the dark mountains. In exile from their own ancestral homes, suddenly deprived of their mankind, and fearing the dire humiliation of subjugation by the vanquishers, in the solitude of their mountain refuge, they came to the desperate resolve to form a women's state. Their first step was to adopt the sacred girdle, that almost universal symbol in the east and Eastern Europe of the unmarried condition; then expelling or mutilating the few males left in their midst, they elected two queens, who alternately presided over home affairs while the other organised defence. But from the defensive the dauntless women soon took the offensive and reconquered their late homes. Such a condition of affairs naturally leading to constant reprisals, the manless state insensibly became organised on a perpetual war footing, an organisation which inevitably led to conquests beyond the original borders. Hence a new problem in statecraft: the ravages of time and the sword woefully thinning the population brought urgently under the attention of their rulers the imminence, more or less postponed by possible recruits, of complete extinction. A remedy had to be found. So truces were periodically declared, and those of the younger members of the state who had slain men in battle, discarding their girdles, visited their neighbours and formed temporary unions, then returning, reassumed the magic circlet. Of the children born of such unions, the males (some report) were sacrificed, or (as others say) mutilated and retained as serfs or sent back to their fathers. The girl babes being fed on mares' milk, on the pith of water-reeds, and as speedily as might be on the flesh of game, were brought up rigorously, and early made acquainted with hardship, with the use of arms, and with horse exercise. They wore a scanty tunic, protected themselves with small shields, and wielded the bow and arrow, the lance and the battle-axe. The better to secure the utmost freedom in archery, the right breast was either amputated or atrophied by searing with red-hot irons, or by close binding; and so the Greeks, when they came into contact with them, called them Amazons, or the breastless. With reminiscences of the steppes of their ancestral home, they cultivated horse exercise assiduously, and are said to have fought equally well on foot and on horseback. Thus were various precautions taken against the dying out of the race.

With a war organisation perfected and adopted as the basis of the social economy, and a population on the increase, conquest became necessary to the community. Great queens arose who led forth the restless swarms. Marpesia is among the first named of these militant rulers, riding at the head of armies to seize upon adjacent kingdoms, making good their hold on the Caucasus. Climbing the comparatively easy northern slopes, they descended the rugged southern declivities and overran Cappadocia, finally settling on the Thermodon, which empties itself into the Euxine (Black Sea), and built thereon their capital of Themyscira, which became the second and greatest cradle of their race. Thence they pushed their way down to the Ægean Sea, swept over most of Asia Minor into Syria, founding many towns, such as Ephesus and Smyrna. We are told of their ever-restless energy, of their organising harassing expeditions, threatening both ancient and rising civilisations, clashing with the armed Trojans in Phrygia, reaching Egypt by way of Syria, and in the train of Dionysus passing through Parthia and so on into India, where, some say, they founded colonies, and then, after harassing the Grecian settlements, flaunted Athens itself.

Ancient writers mostly speak of the Caucasus as a continuation of the Taurus range, entirely within Asia, something far away and little known, but others give graphic descriptions of this the original home of the Amazons. Pliny says that it is "of immense extent, and separating nations innumerable; after taking its first rise at the Indian Sea, it branches off to the north on the right-hand side, and on left towards the south. Then, taking a direction towards the west, it would cut through the middle of Asia were it not that the sea checks it in its triumphant career along the land. It accordingly strikes off in a northerly direction, and forming an arc, occupies an immense track of country, nature, designedly, as it were, every now and then throwing seas in the way to oppose its career: here the Sea of Phœnicia, there the Sea of Pontus; in this direction the Caspian and Hyceanian, [Western and Eastern Caspian], and then opposite to them the Lake Mæotis. Although somewhat curtailed by these obstacles, it still winds along between them, and makes its way even amidst these barriers, and victorious after all, it then escapes with its sinuous course to the kindred chain of the Riphæan mountains. Numerous are the names which it bears, as it is continuously designated by new ones throughout the whole of its course. In the first part it has the name of Imaus [Hindu Kush], after which it is successively known by the names of Emodus, Paropanisus, Circius, Cambades, Paryadres, Choatras, Oreges, Orandes, Niphates, Taurus, and, where it even outtops itself, Caucasus. Where it throws forth its arms as though every now and then it would invade the sea, it bears the name of Sarpedon, Coracesius, Cragus, and then again Taurus. Where it opens and makes passage to admit mankind, it still claims the credit of an unbroken continuity by giving the name of gates to these passes. . . . In addition to this, when it has been cut short in its onward career, it retires to a distance from the seas and covers itself on the one side and the other with the names of numerous nations," so that, among the many others, there were the Amazonian and the Scythian chains. He mentions two flaming mountains (probably due to natural gas or naphtha) in Syria. Strabo places the Amazons among the most eastern developments of the Caucasus, overhanging the Caspian Sea and forming a barrier between the Albanians and Iberians. He also points out that the plains of Scythia and the whole coast of Themyscira, "named the plain of the Amazons," are alluvial, and offer a strange contrast to their mountain refuges. Pliny, speaking of the geography of this

PHIGALIAN FRIEZE, GREEKS AND AMAZONS. BRITISH MUSEUM.

Facing page 28.]

locality in his day, says: "Upon the coast" [of the Euxine] "there is a river Thermodon, which rises at the fortified place called Phanarœa" [Thermea ?] "and flows past the foot of Mount Amazonius" [Mason Dagh ?]. "There was formerly a town of the same name as the river, and five others in all—Amazonium, Themyscira, Satira, Amasia, and Comana." It will be seen from all this the vastness and uncertainty of the whole great black range which connected the Pontus with the far-off regions hidden in a mysterious chaos of mountains, forests, network of rivers and seas and dreary plains.

All the numerous nations referred to above were equally awe-inspiring. Strabo says: "The Amazons are said to live among the mountains above Albania. Good authors, however, say they live at the foot of the Caucasian mountains. When at home, they are occupied in performing with their own hands the work of ploughing, planting, pasturing cattle, and particularly in training horses. The strongest among them spend much of their time in hunting on horseback and practise warlike exercises." In his own day the people living on the south side of the Caucasus were pirates, who left no peace to their neighbours; divided into small tribes, ruled over by tyrants, they lived by brigandage.

Strabo also refers to certain "perfectly barbarous" tribes of the Caucasus who worshipped the earth (the Mother), and offered and ate human sacrifice, though they would neither sacrifice nor eat females of any kind. Clearly the underlying principle impelling these earth-worshippers in this matter was the desire to secure a continuation of species. To this preoccupation we must attribute the honour they meted out to their aged of being strangled by near kinsfolk, here too the males being eaten, while the women were returned to the bosom of the great Mother Earth. The same regard to the bearing principle in nature distinguished the Albanians and Iberians, whom some said were the near neighbours of the Amazons. For these people, though they worshipped chiefly two gods, the sun (Jupiter)—probably "The Unknown God," Creator—and the moon, paid special devotion to the latter, as being the closer influence. There was a temple to the moon near Iberia, and here the priest of the pale goddess was next in importance to the king, and had governance over extensive and popular tracks of sacred land attached to the shrine. Many of the temple attendants and others were given to prophecy. If any one became violently possessed and went about the woods alone, he was seized, bound by the priest in consecrated fetters, and maintained in luxury for a year. Then he was brought forth and placed among the other victims for sacrifice. As the victims stood before the shrine, an attendant of the moon goddess, armed with a sacrificial lance, emerged from the ranks of the encircling crowd, and advancing, struck the sacrifice to the heart, the presiding priest standing by prognosticating from the manner of the fall and the gushing of blood. After which the body was removed to an appointed place, and there trampled upon by the people, so that they might be purified by the gore of the hallowed scapegoat.

Herodotus declares that the Tauri sacrificed all

shipwrecked persons and all Greeks who happened to be driven to take refuge in their ports, these human offerings being made to a virgin goddess. The victim was struck on the head with a club. the head then was severed and nailed to a tree, and the body flung over the rocky cliffs. Prisoners taken in warfare had their heads struck off, which were then placed on tall poles above their houses. Herodotus adds: "The reason that the heads are set up so high is in order that the whole house may be under their protection," which is precisely the same argument used by the head hunters of Borneo and many another savage race. We have earlier hints of this in the ancient "Argonautic," attributed to Orpheus, but almost certainly written by Onomacritus of Athens, who flourished 520–465 B.C. Herein we read much concerning dangerous and ferocious peoples who dwelt round about Lake Mæotis and farther south, among them being the Tauri, a homicidal race, who performed direful sacrifices to Artemis, filling the consecrated cup with human blood. Of the Scythian stock we have terrible tales. They too worshipped the sun and moon and minor gods of the elements—air, fire, water—with sacrificial rites. Scalps of fallen enemies floated as an awful fringe to the bridles of their war-horses. That powerful and mysterious race, the Hittites, came from the Caucasus, and no doubt originally from the same Scythian stock. They worshipped some nature goddess such as Ashtoreth, and their monuments in Asia Minor show that they sacrificed human lives in their religious ceremonies, had guards of priests and priestesses, and observed certain orgies at the vernal season. These Hittites were probably the true founders of Ephesus. They carried the double-headed axe, wore short tunics and high boots with upturned toes. These are snow-shoes, which betray their northern origin. And it is curious to find Pliny writing of dwellers in the higher ranges of the Caucasus who wore boots of untanned leather, with turned-up toes, so that they might walk over the snow. This form of the boot is often seen worn by Amazons depicted on pottery, and is analogous to the Mongolian shoe still worn in China.

Strabo's casual remark as to what the women did "when at home" has almost a sarcastic ring about it, for it would appear as though they were very seldom so peacefully occupied, so varied are their movements, so widespread their influence, according to a general chorus of ancient scribes. In fact, three centuries of ceaseless warfare and adventure are said to have elapsed between the rise of the Amazons and the period of their greatest activity in Asia Minor, when, we are told, the pressure became so intolerable to the Greeks that Bellerophon (redoubtable descendant of Helios, the sun god, and Poseidon, the sea god), fresh from slaying the Chimæra, was sent by the King of Lycia to repel their advance. This task too, like others of great difficulty, he brought to a successful issue, breaking up the Amazon power for the time being.

But events showed that the encroaching power of barbarism had merely been pushed back. Bellerophon gone, the bulwark against the restless

FRIEZE OF MONSOLUS,

Facing page 33.]

tide was removed. Again the Amazonian threat became insistent. Greece was so hard pressed that the queens and their doings rose into an overshadowing prominence, and one of the twelve labours imposed upon Hercules by Erysthesus, king of the Mycenæ, was the extraordinarily hazardous duty of capturing the girdle of the Amazon leader, that girdle which was so thoroughly symbolical of Amazonian ideal, and, therefore, most sacred to them. It was the opening up of great events. Hercules, most of the authors agree, was accompanied on his expedition by Theseus, King of Athens, and the flower of Greek youth, who all embarked on a fleet of splendid galleys. Sailing over the Ægean Sea, they passed through the Bosphorus and Black Sea, and reached the mouth of the Thermodon unmolested. They made their way up the river to Themyscira before Antiope, the home-keeping queen, had time to prepare for effective resistance, or recall Orithya, her sister and co-queen, who was away on some distant war expedition. With all due ceremony, heralds were dispatched by Hercules to Antiope, demanding the surrender of her girdle, which was tantamount to a demand to capitulation, a request promptly refused. So both parties made ready for battle. The Greeks laid siege and attacked in regular form. On their side the weakened garrison of Amazons defended their capital with great obstinacy, and under the leadership of the queen sallied forth to deliver a bloody onslaught. The fighting was fiercest round about Hercules and Theseus. Hercules, invulnerable under his lion's skin, did wondrous deeds, slaying with his own hand eleven Amazon captains who with undaunted valour came on one after the other to the attack. Diodorus Siculus, indeed, tells us that Hercules challenged the foremost of the leaders to single combat. Aëlla, the swift-footed, he slew as she turned and fled; Philippis fell at the first blow; and Prothoe, who had killed many men in hand-to-hand fights, was no luckier; Artemis, the huntress, and several others were quickly tripped up and their spirits sent to the Shades: still Hercules remained untouched. In the end victory rested with the Greeks, who were by no means slow to reap the reward thereof, as their own writers testify. Many prisoners were made and much booty taken. Hercules for his part had captured Menalippe, sister of the two queens, while a fourth sister, Hippolyta, fell into the hands of Theseus. Hercules, mindful of his quest, restored his fair captive in exchange for Antiope's girdle; but Theseus, surrendering to his love for fair Hippolyta, took her as his wife, and decided to carry her off. There are those, Diodorus among them, who say that Hercules put Menalippe to flight, and capturing Antiope, bereft her of her girdle and then handed her over to Theseus, who bore her away to Athens, where she became the mother of Hippolyte. Apollodorus Atheniensis adds a touch of the supernatural. According to him, Hippolyta wore the girdle of Mars, which she was willing to give up to Hercules; but Juno, assuming the form of one of the warrior women, appeared in their midst and stirred up the Amazons to resist the Greeks, whom she declared had come to carry off their queen. Nevertheless, the companion of Jove was unable to stay the Grecian success. Hercules, not content with taking possession of the queen's girdle, also carried off her arms, including her formidable double-headed war-axe, a symbol of leadership of which we shall hear more later on. The Greeks, thus variously loaded with spoils, re-embarked and set sail for home.

When Orithya came hurrying back with her army, it was to find the city in ruins and to listen to the tales of woe uttered by Antiope or Menalippe. Determined to recapture Hippolyta and the other precious spoils, the war queen made an impassioned appeal to her army. What good was it, she asked, for them to be mistresses of Pontus and Asia if, notwithstanding their successes, they remained exposed to the insolence of the Greeks, who dared to flaunt them in the heart of their own state? Were they to submit tamely to murder and rapine? Then, realising the magnitude of her task, she appealed to Sagillus, king of the Scythians, reminding him that they came of the same stock and were threatened by the same ambitious people. This cry for aid was hearkened to, Sagillus dispatching his son Penasagoras at the head of a strong body of horse. Orithya herself gathered a great army, and with her allies marching down the Black Sea coast, passed over that narrow part known as the Cimeran Bosphorus on the winter ice. Others say she marched round the Black Sea, crossing the Danube, and staying long enough on an island called Ares to build a temple which they dedicated to Mars. The lesson seems to be that peril to Greece from the barbarians lay chiefly through an invasion by way of Thessaly. At all events, most of the authors agree that this daring irruption into Attica came by way of Thessaly. Orithya made a swift march, carrying everything before her, though not without occasional sharp fighting. Arriving before the city of Minerva, which then occupied the site of the Acropolis, she encamped her army on ground renowned as the ancient Athens of Cecrops, and then demanded from Theseus the return of Hippolyta and the sacred girdle. Theseus sent her heralds empty away, and, marshalling his army, sacrificed to the god of Fear, whose temple was never opened except in times of grave peril. The Athenian king supplicated the god not to trouble the Greeks, but prayed that he should invade the ranks of the enemy and carry dismay to their hearts.

The siege was close and lasted for upwards of a month, diversified on the one side by sudden sorties, and on the other by fierce assaults; but little of a decisive nature was accomplished until Theseus prepared to sally forth in force. The Amazonian army presented an extended front, the left wing lying far off on a spot subsequently known as the Amazonium, or the plain of the Amazons, the centre occupying the Æreopagus and the right resting on the Pnyx. The Athenians delivered the attack from the Museum, but were turned by the Amazons and driven back to the Temple of Eumenides. Greek reinforcements hurried up from the Palladium, Ardethis, and Lyceum. Then a stubborn hand-to-hand fight took place, the women being so hard pressed that they were at last compelled to seek refuge in their camp. That this feat was only accomplished by putting forth the most strenuous efforts is a point insisted upon by chroniclers. All traditions lay stress on the deadly character of the conflict, and these helped to produce the deep-seated impression so vividly brought home to us when we study the spirited sculptures in which these combats are portrayed. The carnage was terrible and seemed to be never-ending. Both sides fought desperately "for hearth and home," until Hippolyta made her appearance to act as mediatrix between the troops of her victorious but almost exhausted husband, and the defeated, though by no means routed, army of her sister. Ultimately peace was sworn, and the Horcomosin, or Oath House, erected as a memento of the ceremony. Then the slain having received honourable burial, the remnant of the army, having been in Attica some four months, was led back through Greece under a truce. We are told that Hippolyta died and was buried at Megara, where her tomb was long to be seen, while other tombs of Amazons were shown in Athens, in Bœotia, and in Thessaly; but of these, and of the Temple of the Amazons at Athens, no traces have been discovered in modern times.

Certain historians, Plutarch being among the number, hold that Theseus did not accompany Hercules to the Thermodon, that expedition being supposed to have kept the Amazons quiet for a long time. But it is said that Theseus at a later date either invaded the Amazon state in force, or went there by stealth and by stratagem possessed himself of Queen Antiope, by whom he had Hippolyte. These authors hint that the Amazon irruption into

Attica was due to other reasons than the recapture of a girl, and agree that the incursion was a most serious affair. According to these accounts, Antiope when she rushed forward to shield her husband was killed by an arrow shot by Molpadia, who in her turn was slain by Theseus. Otherwise the incidents of the siege are told much in the same way, though some say that it was the Amazons who were driven back to the Temple of the Furies.

If we accept the general version, Orithya's army, beaten—though not without honour, for they were retreating with their arms and under the safeguard of a sworn peace—and having erected images in several temples as thanksofferings, were nevertheless ashamed to go back to Themyscira with the mission unfulfilled. Passing with the male Scythian allies once more through Thessaly, they reached Scythian settlements in Thrace, where a new Amazon state was founded, which later on sent offshoots farther west. Apparently these settlements were formed under laxer laws, for the organisation gradually broke up, and, merging into the surrounding population, this branch of the warrior women returned to a natural mode of life.

Pausanias in his description of Megara states that in his day near the shrine of Pandion in that city there was the tomb of Hippolyta, and he repeats the Megarian account of the events leading up to her death: "When the Amazons marched against the Athenians on account of Antiope, and were vanquished by Theseus, most of them died fighting; but Hippolyta, who was sister to Antiope and at that time held the command of the women, escaped with a few others to Megara. There, however, the disaster which had overtaken her army filled her with despondency at the situation in which she found herself, and with despair of ever returning safe home to Themyscira, she died of grief, and they buried her. Her tomb is shaped like an Amazon shield" (or, according to some renderings, "is adorned with an Amazonian shield").

There was much controversy as to the alleged founding of towns by the Amazons during their incursions into Asia Minor and other quarters. As regards Ephesus, Pausanias corrects Pindar, who attributes the erection of the sanctuary to them. He argues that "it is true that the women from Thermodon, knowing the sanctuary of old, sacrificed to the Ephesian goddess, both on this occasion [when hurrying away from Athens] and when they fled from Hercules, and some of them had sacrificed there at a still remoter time when they fled from Dionysus and sought the protection of the sanctuary. But it was not by them that the sanctuary was founded." This invaluable Murray or Baedeker of the ancient world has much to say that is worth noting, for many of the great public and sacred buildings at Athens, Olympia, and other places were adorned with paintings or sculpture, often by most renowned artists, showing the different events in this momentous war, and Pausanias gives descriptions, though often tantalisingly succinct, of most of these. We cannot do better than follow this guide, who relates what he actually saw and the tales that were current.

At Athens itself there was prominently enough the fine paintings on the walls of the Market Colonnade, representing Theseus and his fellow-Athenians fighting the Amazons, who were mostly shown on horseback. Pausanias comments: "It would appear that their intrepidity was not abated by reverses," for great events awaited the Amazons after Theseus had done with them and had departed to the Shades. These paintings were by the famous Micon, who flourished 460 B.C., and were to be seen down to the middle of the fourth century of our era. "Beside the Gymnasium," says our cicerone, "is a sanctuary to Theseus, with paintings of the Athenians fighting the Amazons." But the great attraction in this matter was on the south wall of the Acropolis, where there were "figures two cubits high, dedicated to Attalus. They represent the legendary war of the giants who once dwelt about Thrace and the Isthmus of Pallone, the fight of the Athenians with the Amazons, the battle with the Medes at Marathon, the destruction of the Gauls at Mysia." It has been conjectured that this Attalus was the second of that name, and, moreover, that these figures, which appear to have been of light-weight bronze (for Plutarch speaks of one of them having been blown over by wind), were reductions from larger sculptures erected to Attalus I. in Asia Minor. Replicas in marble of these have been traced to the museums of the Louvre, Aix, Venice, and Naples, in which last-named place there are recumbent figures of a dead Gaul and an Amazon, who is shown lying on her back, the right leg bent at the knee and partly drawn up.

At Olympia, we are told, most of the deeds of Hercules were shown, and among others his wresting the girdle from the Amazon queen. This was repeated in a sculptured group "not far from the offering of the Acheans," where Hercules was shown fighting the queen, who was on horseback. This group was due to the chisel of Aristocle the Cynodian, whom Pausanias reckons as among the most ancient of the sculptors. In his graphic description of Olympian Zeus, whose statue and throne were adorned with gold, ebony, ivory, and precious stones, he says there was much sculpture and painting. Between the feet of the immense throne were three bars bearing images. On one of these bars "is the troop that fought on the side of Hercules against the Amazons. The total number of figures is twenty-nine. Theseus is arrayed amongst the allies of Hercules." Barrier-like walls kept the populace from passing under the throne, and on three sides of these walls were paintings, the fourth side being blue, like the sky; "the last paintings are Penthesilea giving up the ghost and Achilles supporting her." Then, on the footstool, with its golden lions, was the "battle of Theseus wrought in relief on it. This battle was the first deed of valour done by the Athenians against a foreign foe." Next he tells us that at Pyrrhicus were two temples, one to Artemis-the-putter-of-an-end-to-the-War, because here the Amazons were stopped from further warfare, and the other to Apollo-Amazonius. "Both have wooden images, and tradition says they were votive offerings of the women that came from the Thermodon." Their name crops up again and again in his painstaking itinerary. All of which unmistakably testifies to the importance attributed to these events by the Athenians. To them they were not only memorable wars, but worthy of being commemorated as among the most glorious of their actions. Herodotus, too, makes the Athenians boast of this in their angry war of words with the Tegeans as to which of them should have the honour of occupying the left flank when facing the Persian army. The sons of Athene exclaim: "Another noble deed of ours was that against the Amazons when they came from their seat upon the Thermodon and poured their hosts into Attica." This sentiment of pride in their stand against the fighting women is repeated over and over again. It is, indeed, a sentiment felt in common by the sober chronicler, the poet, and the artist.

Another subject for wonder and admiration on the part of the Greeks is the stubbornness of the Amazons, who, surviving the crushing expeditions of Bellerophon and Hercules, their defeat by Theseus, yet remained as a formidable fighting organisation able to attack near and far kingdoms, and even to venture once more to measure their strength with the Greeks when they met before the walls of Troy. No wonder that Pausanias records with some astonishment: "Their intrepidity was not abated by reverses." We hear of an attack on the Phrygians, who implored assistance from their neighbours, and among others Priam, King of Troy. Long after that war, Priam, when viewing the Greek army from the walls of his doomed capital, told Helen—

> "In Phrygia once were gallant armies known
> In ancient times, when Otreus filled the throne,
> When godlike Mygden led the troops of horse,
> And I, to join them, raised the Trojan force:
> Against the man-like Amazons we stood,
> And Sangar's stream ran purple with their blood."

In spite of this spilling of blood, however, it would seem that the victory remained with the Amazons, for though we are told of the death of their queen Myrina during the campaign, their influence on Persia is one of the points insisted upon by ancient historians, and is supposed to have subsisted down to the days of Alexander of Macedon. Strabo tells us that in the Ilian plain there was a hill dedicated to Myrina, the "Bounding," so called because this enterprising queen was a great horsewoman, who is supposed to have been buried here beneath a great cairn. It was through Phrygia that they invaded Syria and passed into Egypt, though, if we are to accept the legend of their forcing an alliance upon Horus, this must be credited to an earlier expedition, or chronology would be put hopelessly out of joint. Some years after the exploit of Priam on Sangar's gory banks, the Amazons were in alliance with the Trojans against the Greeks; but whether this was due to their admiration of the father-in-law of Helen, or to their undying hatred of the countryman of Bellerophon, Hercules, and Theseus, it is hard to say. At all events, at the call of Priam Penthesilea arrived before Troy with a small band of Amazons, while the venerable king was celebrating the funeral rites of Hector, but recently slain by Achilles. The queen was received with great joy by Priam, who was as much struck by her beauty as by her courage; but Andromache warned this self-confident warrior that she would not find Achilles, who had killed her own lord and many another valiant captain, an easy foe to conquer.

Undaunted by prophecies of evil, Penthesilea,

clothed in light armour and wearing a helmet, armed with sword, bow, and arrows, the formidable double-headed axe in her right hand, a couple of lances and a shield in her left, mounted her charger and went forth to battle at the head of her twelve warriors. As the Amazons advanced, the Greeks stood still, astonished at what they beheld, and somewhat fearful. Penthesilea, throwing a dart by way of signal, dashed to the fray, and with her terrible axe killed eight of the leading Greek captains. But several of the notable Amazons also fell, and the queen redoubled her furious attack, urging her followers and allies to the slaughter. The fight was at its height and the Greeks wavering, when the din of battle reached the ears of Achilles and Ajax, who were offering sacrifice to the manes of Patroclus. Arming themselves, they hastened to the very thick of the mêlée, and endeavoured to stay the advancing tide of Trojan forces. Then the Greek heroes came face to face with the Amazons. Penthesilea, turning to the new arrivals, and recognising them as the most doughty leaders, threw a dart at Achilles, who parried it with his famous shield. Turning her anger against Ajax, the queen again saw her effort frustrated. As the two contending armies paused to watch this heroic duel, Penthesilea advanced, and claiming to be a daughter of Mars, told the Greeks that they were always aggressors, and though their armour had turned aside her avenging darts, they would not be able to escape the wrath she was about to visit upon them with the aid of her axe, which would thus bring relief to groaning Troy. Achilles, on his part, chiding the queen for her vainglorious speech and her unpardonable temerity, told her not to imagine herself invincible, for if she was the daughter of Mars, the Greeks were sons of Jupiter, the lawgiver to gods and men. Hector had fallen to his lance, and she could only hope for a like fate, as the sons of Jupiter were more powerful than the daughters of Mars. So saying, Achilles threw a dart, which pierced her right breast, covering the queen with blood. Then the mighty Greek captain thrust at her horse, and as it fell he vaulted from his own charger, and with his lance ran his prostrate foe through the body. Withdrawing his weapon, he bent over to despoil her of her armour. As he thus stooped over her Achilles was overcome by the glorious beauty of the dying queen, and, reflecting on her courage, he raised Penthesilea gently in his arms, and gazing on her calm face, blamed himself for having dealt the fatal blow to so peerless a creature. The Grecian army stood by in respectful silence; only Thersites ventured to raise his voice to reproach his leader for these softer feelings. Achilles, not deigning to use his weapons against such a creature, struck him in the face with his open hand, hurling him to the ground a dead man. Then once more raising the lifeless body of the Amazons' queen, he gave it into the honourable keeping of the Trojans.

It is one of the incidents that most deeply impressed itself upon Hellenic thought and its expression in art. It formed the central motive of the "Æthiopia" of Arctinus of Miletus, long supposed to be a precursor of the Homer cycle, but who really flourished about 770 B.C., and whose great poem was a continuation of the "Iliad." Indeed, it was occupied with describing the combats between the Greeks and the Amazons and the final acts of Achilles. Tradition says that its finest passages related to the great duel between the Amazon queen and the Greek leader, the latter's anger followed swiftly by sentiments of respect and pity as he contemplated the beautiful woman whom he had slain. The "Æthiopia" has only come down to us in insignificant fragments, though its influence is seen prominently both in literature and art, where it represents the later feelings of the Grecians when they had grown out of the terrors that had inspired the growth of the myth.

Quintus Smyrnœus probably gives the best rendering of this last legend, though he adds certain marvels. According to him, Penthesilea is moved not so much by hatred against the Greeks as from a personal grief, she having accidentally killed her sister while out hunting. So

> "Her crime to expiate, with her sword
> To offer victims to the Furies dire,
> Who, tho' unseen, pursu'd her to avenge
> Her sister's blood ; for with unwearied speed
> They chase the guilty, tracking all their steps."

Spurred on by this terrible need for atoning by offering human victims to the ghost of the dead and to the outraged deities, Penthesilea goes forth with her twelve companions, and is welcomed by Priam. On the fatal morn,

> "when Aurora, rosy-ankled, smil'd,
> Penthesilea left her couch, and cloth'd
> Her limbs in armour sheen, the gift of Mars ;
> First to her snowy legs she fitted close
> The golden greaves, and on her tender breast
> Bound the strong plate of variegated mail.

Then from her shoulder the huge sword she slung
Proudly, its sheath all exquisitely wrought
With ivory and silver. Next she took
Her crescent buckler, like the horned moon,
When, gleaming o'er the waves, she climbs the sky
With half-replenished lamp. Her helmet last,
Its nodding crest beropt with gold, she plac'd
Upon her head. In this array she shone
Refulgent, as the forky fires that Jove
Hurls to earth, the red vaunt-couriers
Of the big rain-drops, and the roaring winds.
In her left hand, behind the shield, she bore
Two jav'lins snatched in haste, and in her right
An axe with double edge, which Discord gave
To the maiden's great defence in war."

Then she hurries to the fray, carrying slaughter among the Greeks, and at last espying Achilles and Ajax, she flies to meet them, and after the inevitable war of words, she is slain by Achilles, who, stooping to remove her armour,

"felt exceeding grief
As on the body of the maid he gaz'd,
Mourning her not less than for the death
Of his belov'd Patroclus."

Quintus adds that Mars rushed down from Olympus, alighting on Mount Ida, which rocked and streamed with fire, and the war god would have attacked the Greeks had he not been restrained by the thunder and lightning of angered Jove.

In all this we see the Greek feeling as to the inevitableness of tragedy. Mere mortals are driven by Fate, the sport of the gods, while struggling with this sentiment there peeps out the old cruel doctrine that outraged gods can be appeased alone by personal or vicarious sacrifice of life. And so the scene closes on a note of pity.

CHAPTER III

THE AMAZONS OF ANTIQUITY—(*continued*)

MUCH as these writers had to say of the Amazons in the era of their glory, they are equally eloquent and entertaining when dealing with the wondrous women in the days of the community's decadence. One of the most picturesque incidents relates to the Amazonian hatred for the Greeks. After the death of Achilles and the fall of Troy, we are told, the dead captain-demigod reigned over an enchanted isle in the Black Sea at the mouth of the Danube, which must, therefore, have been close to that Isle of Ares where the Amazons, on their way to Athens, erected a temple to the god of war. When Thetis was lamenting over the funeral pyre of Achilles, Neptune consoled her by the promise—

> "There is an island in the Euxine Sea
> Where, by my power, Achilles shall be deem'd
> A god ; and him with sacrificial rites
> The neighbouring nations shall adore."

Whatever the exact position of the island may have been, tales of the glory of this shadowy kingdom reached the Amazons in their capital on the Thermodon, and there, maddened by fierce hatred for Queen Penthesilea's slayer, they determined to follow the hero even in this dominion of ghosts. So they

SECTION OF PHIGALEIAN FRIEZE. COMBAT OF GREEKS AND AMAZONS.
BRITISH MUSEUM.

Facing page 48.]

laid violent hands on certain navigators who came up the river, and compelled them to build a fleet of galleys. They embarked thereon a strong force of horse, and bade the sailors to steer them to the mysterious isle. The vengeful and impious armada reached the beautiful shores clothed with stately groves. A safe landing was effected, but as the Amazons approached a magnificent temple half hidden in a luxuriantly growing wood, their horses gave every sign of anxiety, which, as they advanced, waxed into ungovernable terror. Curveting and rearing, they threw their exhausted riders, who, as they lay on the ground, were trampled upon and bitten by the demented steeds as they turned and bolted to the cliffs, where, not pausing an instant, they dashed themselves to destruction among the raging waves. A terrific storm of wind and lightning sprang up, involving the Amazons in the havoc created by the raging tempest. Few escaped the warring elements to convey the tidings to Themyscira.

Apollonius Rhodius in his "Argonautic" gives us glimpses of two forms of Amazons. He tells how the bold navigators going in search of the Golden Fleece visited the island of Lemnos, which they found inhabited solely by women and ruled over by the gentle Hypsipile. Jason and his companions were received with a considerable show of suspicion, for the women appeared in battle array—

> "Hypsipile assum'd her father's arms
> And led the van, terrific in her charms."

But when it became evident that the Argonauts had no evil intentions, the youthful queen told them a pitiful tale. Lemnos, she said, had been invaded and all the men killed. This was not an account to raise the suspicions, though it might kindle the pity, of the Greeks, who were invited to stay in the island and fill the places of the slain. The truth was, however, that the men of Lemnos had been killed by their own womenkind, a crime brought about by a neglect of the gods. Venus, forgotten by the women, took her revenge by causing them to become obnoxious to their husbands and lovers, who, turning in loathing away from them, brought girl slaves from the mainland. Angered by this course of affairs, the women slew all males and the slaves, then assumed arms, daily expecting that, their exploits having been noised abroad, men from adjacent countries would come to punish them. To the guilty spouses and daughters the Argonauts as they first appeared were a cause of dread, then, as their pacific intentions became known, a source of hope; and so the women did their best to make the intrepid explorers forget their dangerous quest. However, after some little delay, the Argonauts sailed away, and passing through the Hellespont, creeping up the Euxine, they wisely

> "flee the Amazonian shore,
> Else Themyscira soon, with rude alarms,
> Had seen th' assembled Amazons in arms."

Such was the repute of these women, who were more to be dreaded than the armies, powerful kings, and magic spells Jason and his following had to face.

Of another momentous maritime adventure we have many details from Herodotus, who, speaking of the Sauromatœ, says that after the battle of Thermodon, which was the second strenuous effort of the Greeks to drive back the women barbarians, three galleys were loaded by Hercules with Amazon prisoners. These galleys becoming separated from the fleet, they sailed for the Bosphorus on the way to Greece; but suddenly the prisoners mutinied, and succeeded in killing their guards and the sailors. It was a victory which threatened to cost them dear, for the women, having slain the navigators, found themselves helpless owing to their lack of knowledge of ships, which drifted about at the mercy of the elements. The galleys were blown in a northerly direction, and passing through dangerous straits, reached the Palus Mæotis (Sea of Azof), there running ashore close to certain "white cliffs," which have not been identified. Scrambling ashore on a strange coast, the women seized the first herd of horses they encountered, and thus mounted, feeling more at home, began exploring the surrounding country. They fell upon the unsuspecting Scythians, slaughtering and pillaging right and left. The Scythians could not tell who these raiders were: dress, language, and all were quite unfamiliar to them. On the other hand, the Amazons mistook the shaven inhabitants for bands of youths. But in the fights some of the Amazons fell, and then the truth was revealed, and this made the men loath to repel the invaders with arms, so they hit upon a deep and poetic stratagem. They sent youths, lightly armed, to watch them. Camping at some distance from the Amazons, following their every movement at a respectful distance, the chances of the chase brought members of the two forces together; and as the youths did all in their power to show their pacific intentions, the camps gradually drew nearer. There were meetings, designed on the part of the young men, and at last the warrior women, realising that there was no danger from this quarter, hastened opening up communications, with the result that what could not be done by Scythian valour was speedily accomplished by the sarkless blind boy with his invisible darts. Mistrust gave way before love, the two camps blended, and the women soon acquired the local tongue. Then the youths desired to go home and settle down—they wanted no other wives than the Amazons. But to this proposal their companions replied: "We could not live with your women—our customs are quite different to theirs. To draw the bow, to hurl the javelin, to bestride the horse, these are our arts—of womanly employments we know nothing. Your women, on the contrary, do none of these things, but stay at home in their wagons, engaged in womanish tasks, and never go out to hunt or to do anything. We should never agree!" So they suggested that the young men should go to their parents and ask them for their inheritance, to enable them to form separate camps. This the youths agreed to do, and coming back with their property, ceded by the politic fathers, offered it to the strange women. Then these said that they were ashamed to remain in the country, for, not content with killing and robbing the inhabitants, they had now stolen sons from their fathers: to dwell in peace they would have to go elsewhere.

This also was agreed upon. Crossing the Tanais, they journeyed eastward a distance of three days north from that stream, and then again northward another three days' march. From this it would appear that the camp was first formed in what is now Europe, but the new nation subsequently moved north-east.

Herodotus adds: "The women of the Sauromatœ have continued from that day to the present to observe their ancient customs, frequently hunting on horseback with their husbands, sometimes even unaccompanied, in war taking the field, and wearing the very same dress as the men." It was of these people that Pliny also had much to say. We are here on somewhat more solid ground, and can see how the marvellous grew out of the natural. Certainly this account of Herodotus destroys the extravagant claims put forth by some historians as to the widespread nature of the Amazonian conquests. For, after all, the Palus Mæotis is not very far from the Thermodon, and, as we see, Herodotus makes both parties absolutely unknown to each other, which could scarcely have been the case if we follow Diodorus Siculus or Apollonius Rhodius and many another of the rhetorical school of writers. Some foundation there was, however, for there is no smoke without fire.

We must not wonder too much that all kinds of traditions concerning the Amazons lingered on. References to them in many directions are found in the pages of chronicles and geographical treatises. Justinus says that when Alexander the Great was in Hyrcania he was visited by Thalestris, queen of the Amazons, who came at the head of 300 horsewomen, travelling twenty-five days through populous and dangerous countries to ask favours from the Macedonian conqueror. She remained thirteen days with Alexander, and returning to her country, died shortly after, and with her passed away the glory of her race. Quintus Curtius is even more circumstantial, but Arrian says Thalestris, who, according to him, came with a following of 100 Amazons all armed with double-headed axes and carrying half-moon shields, was sent as a present to Alexander by the governor of the neighbouring province. Arrian quotes with caution, and says that if these women did really come into the Macedonian camp, they must have been other warriors than the famous Amazons, in which opinion others agree with him, while many altogether dispute the truth of the alleged incidents. Plutarch says that Clitarchus, Policritus, Onesicritus, Antigenes, Ister, and several more give the story as an authentic fact, while Aristobulus, Chares of Theangela, Ptolemy, Anticlides, Philo the Theban, Philip of Theangela, Hecatœus of Eretria, Philip of Chalcis, and Duris of Samos treated the matter as a pure fable. He reports that Lysimachus, ridiculing the story when read out to him by Onesicritus, laughingly asked, "Where was I at that time?" which Plutarch thinks conclusive coming from so important a lieutenant of Alexander, one who must have been privy to any such event.

Though we hear of women coming armed into battle long after the conquests of Alexander, we are told very little more about the Amazons by the Greeks themselves.

Many of the later Greek writers treated the whole Amazon story as a myth, to be placed on the same level as the gigantomachia, the tales of the Gorgons, centaurs, and so on; which is probably true—that is to say, they must be looked upon as symbolical exaggerations of certain ancient facts. Strabo, Herodotus, and Pliny have been blamed by these later authors for giving credit to the legends. This is not fair so far as regards Strabo. No doubt he has much to say about the Amazons, their places of dwelling and their exploits, but in all this he is merely acting as reporter, recording the opinions of other authors and local traditions. Of his own attitude to the subject there can be no doubt, for in an outspoken passage he says: "There is a peculiarity in the history of the Amazons. In other histories the fabulous and the historical parts are kept distinct. For what is ancient, false, and marvellous is called fable. But history has truth for its object, whether it be old or new, and it either rejects or rarely admits the marvellous. But with regard to the Amazons, the same facts are related both by modern and ancient writers; they are marvellous, and exceed belief. For who can believe that an army of women, or a city, or a nation, could ever subsist without men? and not only subsist, but make inroads upon the territories of other people, and obtain possession not only of the places near them, and advance as far as the present Ionia, but even dispatch an expedition across the sea to Attica?" Plutarch, as we have seen, while discrediting the story of Thalestris's visit to Alexander, is not found among those who doubt the existence of the Amazon state, as may be gathered particularly in his handling of the life of Theseus. While we need have little compunction in regarding Quintus Curtius and Diodorus Siculus as romancers, the reports recorded in such manner as Strabo and Herodotus do must cause us to hesitate before passing a rash judgment, and send us to inquire into the philosophy of the obscure subject.

Both writers and artists have given a fairly consistent idea of the costumes and equipments of the Amazons. In the early stages of their history they wore a scanty chiton, or tunic, caught up at the waist by the celebrated girdle, so that it scarcely reached the knees, the upper part being fastened over the left shoulder, leaving the right breast bare. But at a later period the robe is more ample and flowing, which probably denoted the transition from the habit of fighting on foot to the general use of the horse. It is said that the early chitons were nothing more than the skins of beasts killed in hunting. Strabo specially mentions that "they make helmets and coverings for the body, and girdles, of the skins of wild animals." Of course untanned pelts have in all times and places been used for clothing, for the special reason that they afforded some sort of defence against darts and other weapons; so the use of skins of wild beasts in Asia, and of serpents in the case of the African women, merely pointed to their power having arisen while they were still in the early barbarous stages of development. In art, with the possible exception of the primitive fictile specimens, however, the drapery is generally of the nature of a textile. For defensive armour they are given low breastplates, sometimes, in the late examples, the queens' cuirasses being adorned with the Medusa mark; greaves for the front parts of the legs, thigh plates, and helmets. The helmets at first appear to be of the Minerva type, tall, with the protecting comb, and often plumed; then they are lighter, more approaching the shape of the head; and after the Eastern adventures the high kidaris or Phrygian-like cap, occasionally with points falling over the ears and the nape of the neck, is worn. To the greaves are added sandles, a strap over the ankle to hold the spur, and in default of leg armour the lacings of the sandle may be carried half-way up to the knee. Sometimes we see, as in the interesting fragment of terra-cotta in the Towneley Collection at the British Museum, Amazons in short chitons and wearing high boots with turned-over tops and lion's face at the front and turned-up toes, which footgear is suggestive of Eastern influence. In the best specimens of art the feet and legs are bare, only the ankle strap for the spur being shown. After the conquests in Phrygia and expeditions to Persia, we find the Amazons in Persian raiment, consisting of close-fitting tunic and trousers, high boots, and either skull-cap helmets or the kidaris. Their shields, known as the pelta, are small, and either half-moon shaped or showing a double crescent, the outer edge forming a nearly complete circle, while the inner one is dented so as to present two concave curves and three horns; often, however, we see the completely circular target. All these three forms have been regarded as lunar emblems.

Their offensive arms consisted of the bow and arrow, the dart, javelin, and the long lance, the latter being merely the adaptation of the missile spear to the need of cavalry fighting at close quarters. A characteristic weapon was the double-headed axe, to which many attributed a symbolical meaning. It was undoubtedly looked upon as an emblem of authority, originally of divine authority, being analogous to the double thunderbolt. As a weapon, it was of Asiatic origin, and appears to have been introduced into Asia Minor by the terrible Hittites. It created great terror among both Greeks and Romans when first met with by those fighting races in the hands of Eastern hordes. Quintus Smyrnus repeats a tradition that Hercules, having ravished the sacred double-headed axe from the Amazonian queen, bestowed it on Omphale, Queen of Lydia. It is said that the axe was preserved as an emblem of regality down to the days of Candaules, last of the Heraclidæ. The sword is only rarely mentioned in connection with the Amazons, which points to extreme antiquity, or at least primitive customs. Of their skill with the bow and arrow many are the wondrous tales that are recorded. Their darts flew as rapid as a glance, as quick as thought, and so the soldiers of Marcus Crasus at a much later date said of the "strange sort of arrows" used against them by the Parthians. These weapons, the distressed Romans found, were "swifter than lightning, reaching their mark before you can see they are discharged." The barbarians drew the arrows to the feather, and let fly with such force that they pierced light armour, fastening feet to the ground, pinning hands to shields as they transfixed the enemies' limbs. Much the same is told us of the women warriors, for there was little protection against their strength, unless the magic of the Nemean lion's skin or a talismanic shield was there to protect a Hercules or an Achilles.

At first, according to the accounts, tactics similar to those of the old Scythians and Parthians fighting at a distance, common, indeed, to most of the early barbarians, were adopted. There was a swift rush forward, a discharge of arrows and darts, and then a speedy retreat, but a retreat which was as dangerous to the enemy as an advance, for they covered their strategic movements to the rear by a flight of arrows, aiming over their shoulders or turning half round as they fled. Every arrow had its billet. As Plutarch says of the Parthians and Scythians : "It is indeed an excellent expedient, because they save themselves by retiring, and, by fighting all the while, escape the disgrace of flight." This retreat and advance seems to have been accompanied by a mazy dance as part of the tactics, in which swiftness and uncertainty of movement was the essential factor. We are told that, besides the use of trumpets, they advanced to combat to the music of the systrum, which would be in keeping with the semi-sacred, semi-barbarous dance, the waving helmet plumes, and the startling Medusa heads on the leaders' shields. With their wider conquests we find a partial abandonment of the swift advance and retreat strategy, which was supplemented by the advance in force, entailing the adoption of the lance and double-headed axe for use at close quarters. But, as we have said, the sword was rarely associated with the Asiatic Amazons. From early times the horse was made the companion of the youthful warrior, and the prowess of the Amazons on horseback won the admiration of all beholders, when it did not inspire terror. Theirs was always light cavalry, the horses practically without trappings save a simple bridle, and swift manœuvring being adhered to. They used the bow and arrow and the dart, as well as the lance and axe, when mounted, aiming backwards as they retreated, and even vaulting round on the horses' backs to fight, facing the enemy though retiring. So artists have depicted the Amazons, and sculptors too have shown us these and many other tricks, which we know are quite consistent with barbarian tactics. It was one of the Greek ways of insisting upon the origin of these warriors from the bleak steppes. And so we are told that when the prisoners escaped from the galleys of Hercules, their first action on landing on the Sarmatian shore was to seize horses, and then, like wildly beautiful she-centaurs, descend with disconcerting suddenness upon the unsuspecting inhabitants.

In the writings of certain authors we find brief allusion to the use of nets among Amazons when in battle, the nets being thrown over enemies, who were then strangled or dispatched with the lance. No doubt this accretion to the picturesque legends is due to a poetical metaphor, symbolising either entanglement through feminine wiles, or the bewildering enveloping movements of the agile warriors, who harassed the enemy on all sides, but swiftly retired to renew the attack, so that they encompassed their opponents like the meshes of a net, out of which there appeared to be no way, for, subtly yielding, they could not be reached or cut through. That barbarian gladiators (the retiarii, who carried tridents) did use nets in combats in the arena we know, but there is no mention of their employment in actual warfare. On the other hand, the use of entangling nets and knotted thongs by gods and supernatural creatures in their struggles among themselves or against man is a commonplace in most mythologies, and is closely associated with incantations and magic.

All these niceties of detail have reached us through the minor lights of art and literature, for it is to be observed that in the best of Greek art that has come down to us the Amazons are always treated with pleasing simplicity. The costume generally consists of short tunic; the arms, legs, head, and part of the bust are bare, though occasionally in the later sculptures the chiton is worn long, reaching well below the knee, and is somewhat ample, while sandles are shown. There is little evidence of defensive armour beyond the rare use of helmets and the small shield. The weapons are the bow and arrow, the lance, and the double-headed axe. Elaboration only comes into minor art. No doubt this studied simplicity was largely due to the desire to convey an idea of the remoteness of the scenes shown; so the Greek warriors are seen either entirely naked or very scantily clad, though they wear fine helmets and carry large shields.

CHAPTER IV

Amazons in Far Asia

Amazons as portrayed for us by the Greeks belonged, at all events in the fulness of their development, to Asia Minor, we might almost say to Pontus, yet traditions of their excursions to the Farthest East existed. Certainly the idea of the woman fighter and the female community is very generally diffused.

As for the women of the Thermodon, while many held that the remnants of the Themysciran hosts had wandered beyond the Tanais, there were long persistent rumours of their having taken refuge in the fastnesses of the Caucasus, and having made their way thence to Persia, Tartary, and the east. Thus some of those writers who chronicle the visit of Thalestris to Alexander when he was in Hyrcania suppose that she may have belonged to an Asiatic offshoot from the Caucasus, whence the tribe had spread yet farther afield. However, the more we journey eastward the less easy does it become to distinguish between the migratory and the local legends.

Mountains and forests seem to have been the favourite places of refuge for the Amazons, the great alluvial plains the seats of their growth and power. But we also discover a widespread tendency to locate their colonies on islands, partly, no doubt, on account of their remoteness, though, as we shall endeavour to prove, largely owing to more or less clear observation often obscured by too sweeping deductions. While we find the early Portuguese voyagers and their competitors placing a colony of these women in Socotra or some island, or islands, off the south-east coast of Africa, Marco Polo, the Venetian traveller, who wrote late in the thirteenth century, tells us of certain dual islands off the coast of India. He says: "When you leave this kingdom of Kesmacoran (Mekran), which is on the mainland, you go by sea some 500 miles towards the south, and then you find the two islands, Male and Female, lying about thirty miles distant from one another. The people are all baptized Christians, but maintain the ordinances of the Old Testament: thus when their wives are with child they never go near them till their confinement, and for forty days thereafter. In the island, however, which is called Male, dwell the men alone, without their wives or any other women. Every year when the month of March arrives the men all set out for the other island, and tarry there for three months,—to wit, March, April, May,—dwelling with their wives for that space. At the end of those three months they return to their own island, and pursue their husbandry and trade for the other nine months. . . . As for the children which their wives bear them, if they be girls, they abide with their mothers; but if they are boys, the mothers bring them up till they are fourteen, and then send them to their fathers. Such is the custom of the two islands. The wives do nothing but nurse their children and gather such fruit as their island produces, for their husbands do furnish them with all necessaries." All of which offers a striking contrast to the social economy usually attributed to the Amazons. Instead of the women being trained and equipped for warfare, we have a peace organisation, so that the whole appears to us little more than an exaggeration of common facts.

We are told that these people lived on flesh and rice; that there was plenty of ambergris cast up on the shores; that the men were excellent fishers; and, moreover, that they dwelt in islands far from the mainland. Now, under such conditions as these, in a small community, the men would probably be away from home at regular seasons for months together, pursuing their avocations of rice cultivation, fishing, and barter, and then the home island would be populated chiefly, if not entirely, by women and children. Added to this a possible adherence to Old Testament law (Marco Polo says that the islands had a bishop who was subject to the Archbishop of Socotra, whose Christianity would, no doubt, be somewhat akin to that of the Copts), or some analogous heathen custom, and we have a perfectly comprehensible explanation of the story. To this day we can easily discover innumerable "dual" colonies of this description during such seasons as local industries make migration on the part of the larder-fillers imperative. But the Venetian's story, taken literally, was a fruitful source of many embellished yarns, which long beguiled a wonder-loving world.

Marco Polo, it must be confessed, was merely

taking up the running, for the legend, in one form or another, is extremely old. Hiuen Tsang is one of the best known of these raconteurs. He was a Chinese Buddhist priest, who spent fifteen years of his life, between 629 and 645 A.D., in a pilgrimage through India. Probably he is the greatest traveller who ever visited the land and recorded his experiences; for he passed through the country from Kabul to Kashmir, to the mouths of the Ganges and the Indus, from Nepal to Kanchipura, near Madras, and was only deterred from sailing over to Ceylon owing to the disturbed state of the island following on the recent death of the king. Although Hiuen Tsang did not visit Ceylon, he gave a quaint account of its early history. He reports that in the distant ages a certain boy and girl were born on the mainland, their mother being a princess and their father a lion (shall wè say, the result of a mésalliance between a rajah's daughter and some doughty chieftain of a forest-robber race?). After many adventures that hardly concern us, but including the slaying of the man-lion by his son, the youth and maid are cast adrift in two boats. The boy landed in Ceylon, which was so rich in gems that it was henceforth to be known as the Isle of Precious Stones. The sister found herself high and dry on another part of the island, and becoming acquainted with evil spirits, brought forth 500 daughters, who were rhackshasis, or female demons who lived on men's flesh. These rhackshasis were extremely beautiful and lived in a magnificent fortress of iron, over which floated a magic flag, which quivered voluptuously in the breeze when luck was to befall the community, but drooped when disaster threatened. To this castle surmounted by its piratical signal the bewitching women lured men, who, after a brief dalliance as soothing as it was delusive, found themselves incarcerated in dungeons, there to await their turn to form a meal for their lady-loves.

A fatal day came, however, when the rhackshasis cajoled a party of rich merchants to their gorgeous home. All unconscious, the men played their part, little guessing the fate reserved for them. But by chance the leader of the trading band, wandering about the fortress precincts, approached a dark spot, and was attracted by piteous lamentations. Investigating the matter, he was horrified to learn that the dungeons were filled with men, who once had sported with the dames, but now awaited a terrible doom. There was, however, hope for the men who were yet free. The prisoners had learnt too late that on the seashore there dwelt a divine horse, who, if sufficiently implored, would ferry the beseechers across to the mainland. So without a moment's delay the merchant gathered his companions, and all turning their faces shoreward, prayed the horse to help them. Thereupon the equine divinity appeared, and bidding them cling to his mane and never look back, plunged into the sea with his living load. It was not a moment too soon, for the women, missing their male companions, rushed to the water's edge, and weeping aloud, called on their lovers to return. Seeing that this had no effect, they picked up their baby sons and flew through the air, crying and beseeching all the way, and finally landing where the horse landed. But on the mainland they were powerless, the men remaining deaf to their appeals, blind to their blandishments. Then the queen rose in the air and flew straight to the home of the leading merchant. There she told a sorrowful tale of her marriage to the precious son of the house; of his departure for unknown lands and the arrival of tidings of his death; and of her utter despair at being left in poverty with her fatherless boy. As they wept over his suffering, the parents of the missing man took pity on her, giving her shelter. Then the merchant returned, and refusing to listen to the rhackshasis, turned her out of doors, whereupon misfortunes quickly overwhelmed the house. The king of the land, hearing of the wonderful beauty of the strange woman, and welcoming her to his palace, turned his wrath upon the unfortunate merchant. Disaster upon disaster followed, involving all concerned, and the kingdom was in a sad plight. When matters were at their worst, the king was met by the divine horse, who opened the monarch's eyes to the kind of creature he was harbouring. The rhackshasis was seized, a great army assembled, and Ceylon was invaded, the demon women—who had given up in despair when they saw their enchanted flag hang disconsolate round the staff—being destroyed.

An earlier pilgrim, Fa Hsien, another Chinese Buddhist priest, who lived in India for a space of fourteen years, only returning home in 413 A.D., actually visited Ceylon, and calls it the Land of Lions, which is interesting in view of the preceding legend. Fa Hsien too heard faint echoes of some prehistoric period, and reported thereon that the island was originally inhabited by "devils, spirits, and dragons." Even in those early days, at a period anterior to the advent of Buddha, merchants from the mainland traded with the uncouth islanders, though the devils and spirits did not appear in person. Their methods of dealing were far more delicate than the usual market-haggling, for they trustfully spread out their goods on the shore, duly ticketing each piece or heap with the price they should fetch, and the merchants, having made their selections and deposited the exchange value, departed. These, indeed, must have been tolerably *bons diables*, and probably their rhackshasis nature only made itself manifest when the wily Hindu or his precursor proved but indifferently honest. To the more civilised mainlander the small black island aborigines would appear uncanny "devils," though profitable trafficking might be carried on with them. This would be difficult enough owing to their extreme wildness and the timidity of the forest and mountain folk, who moved about like will-o'-the-wisps, and only became formidable when ill-treated or robbed. On the other hand, the feminine arts brought to bear on the visitors, who would be susceptible in spite of their cupidity, would naturally be attributed to sorcery, and the whole story ultimately assume the picturesque and marvellous form in which it is presented to us by Hiuen Tsang.

These Ceylon rhackshasis, although of local parentage, are merely a variant of the vampire women so commonly met with, at least in the realms of fancy, and of whom Circe and the Syrens are types, and whose analogues may be found in Norse and Teutonic mythology. Of the early eastern exploits of the Themysciran Amazons we are told in connection with the legends of Dionysus, that protean hero-god who represents springtide and the arts of husbandry, more especially the wealth of the vine. Of him, it must be remembered, the poets say that this "twice born" was brought up at Nicæa, went to the rescue of his father Jupiter in the war against Saturn and the Titans, sharing in the success, aided, some say, by the valiant Amazons. With them he went through Asia as far as India, and on his way back took in Egypt as part of his conquest. Dionysus of the earlier Greek fables was a handsome youth. Then we know him as a beautiful hero, glorying in his eastern exploits and bringing back the vine, which had been destroyed during the Deucalion deluge. Wherever he went, and was received, he brought with him prosperity. His Amazonian guard appears to symbolise his sterner aspects. Undoubtedly it was this phase of the myth that was uppermost in the minds of many observant travellers in India. For instance, Niebuhr, describing the rich profusion of carvings on the rock-hewn temples of Elephanta, says: "One woman has but a single breast, from which it should be seen that the story of the Amazons was not unknown to the old Indians." He gives a picture of this supposed Amazon, of which many examples may be found scattered up and down India wherever Brahmanical influence has made itself felt. The truth is, this is no Amazon, but the mighty Ard-dhanarishwara, representing the union of the "moon-crested" god Shiva with the female principle Uma, or of his wife Parvati. Many are the stories, full of philosophical meaning, told of this dual personality, teaching that the complete life cannot be one-sided, the sexes being interdependent. It is a sermon in stone telling of life and toleration, and, therefore, is in exact opposition to the warnings conveyed by the original Amazon myths; also differing from the Talmudist account of Adam's first appearance as a man-woman of monstrous size and a terror to the angels. Both the eastern allegories tell of the unity of nature, though they travel along divergent roads. Yet, united and separate, the Indian mystic duality are not without their grimness, for they represent the great natural forces and the supernatural and their unfathomable workings. Shiva is "he of whom growth" (increase, prosperity) "is," the "wearer of the eight forms"—that is, the personification of earth, water, air, fire, ether, the sun, the moon, and sacrifice. Parvati is the universal, the nature goddess. The religious books say that Shiva and Parvati were one in body, united like the *word* and the *sense*.

According to one of the Puranas, Arddhanarishwara sprang "full armed," like another Pallas Athene, from the wrinkled brow of Brahma the Creator, who ordered a division, so that Shiva and Parvati came into separate existence. In another of the Puranas we find that after marriage Shiva and Parvati lived on Mount Kailasa, where the wife kept house and the divine husband supported his family by begging. But Shiva smoked too liberally of the intoxicating herbs, and neglected his task of mendicancy, whereupon Parvati reproved him, sent him forth to beg, and then carried off their children to her father the Himalayas. But repenting, she assumed the form of Anna-purna, goddess of food, and laid an embargo on all eatables in any house where Shiva sought charity, so that he was sent empty away. On reaching home, the famished and disheartened Shiva was welcomed by Parvati with smiles, and she bestowed food on him. Then he embraced her, and they became one. Whatever the version, the lesson of toleration and interdependence is laid down.

In the Elephanta carving the differences of sex are given great prominence with true Oriental love of exaggeration. The figure is 16 feet 9 inches high, the right side being Shiva, the left Uma. Each half has two arms. In the case of Shiva, the back hand holds up one of his most venerated symbols, the hooded cobra, while the other rests on the head of Nandi, the sacred bull steed. Dr. Wilson declared that it represents not the domesticated bullock, but the wild *bos gavœus* of the forests, which goes far to prove the antiquity of these carvings, or of their prototypes. The head-dress is of the usual high and much-decorated pattern. On the right is the crescent, and under the cap the hair is represented by a series of little knobs; on the left two heavy folds descend to Uma's shoulder, and the hair is shown in rows of neat ringlets. Uma holds up a large mirror, which Niebuhr and others, with their notion of Greek influence, mistook for a small round shield. The feminine side of Arddhanarishwara is, therefore, distinctly associated with the arts of peace, not with those of war or governance.

It is curious that the Latins of the third century of our era possessed a truer account of those carvings than we did in the eighteenth century. A part of Porphory's lost treatise *De Styge* has been preserved, and this relates to the questioning of certain Indians who came into Syria during the reign of Heliogabalus. These Indians spoke about a vast natural cave in a lofty mountain. "And," said they, "in this cave there is a statue which was about ten or twelve cubits. It stands upright, with the hands extended in the form of the cross. And the right of its face is that of a man, while the left is that of a woman. Now in the same way the right arm too, and the right foot, and the whole half are of a man, and the left of a woman : so that on seeing it we are astonished that we can see the dissimilarity of the two sides in one body without division. In this statue, they say, are carved round the right the sun, round the left the moon ; and down the two arms are cleverly carved a number of angels and all the things that exist in the universe—that is, the heaven, the mountains and the sea, and the river and ocean, and plants and animals, and, in a word, all things that are. This statue, they say, God gave his son when creating the universe, that he might have a model." They also declared that the statue sweated in summer unless fanned by the priests ; but we must remember that originally the statue was painted black or blue on the right, vermilion on the left, or yellow and white, and this painting may have had something to do with the phenomena. The angels and other decorative accessaries are not on but behind the statue. This divergence may be due to a misunderstanding on the part of the interrogators, and so with a few other inaccuracies. But the particulars given seem to point clearly to Elephanta, and if this is so, then we have evidence of a much earlier date than the tenth, or even the eighth, century, which modern students of Indian antiquities are inclined to assign to the carvings. It will be seen that the pilgrims from India gave their Roman questioners a true notion of the elemental and religious character of these carvings, which had nothing to do with any Amazonian polities.

Nevertheless, warlike women were well known in India. We hear of them from Greek sources by way of Megathenes, who was there as ambassador about 300 B.C. On the death of Alexander in Babylonia, one of his successful lieutenants who struggled to grasp the Eastern power usurped by the great Macedonian was Seleukotos Nikador, who ultimately became master of Babylonia, Bactria, and lord of Western and Central Asia. But when he reached India, he found himself confronted by a powerful native chief, who, revolting against the Greek and other foreign governors, had assumed imperial power, with his seat of government at Pataliputra (modern Patna). This Indian, whom the natives knew as Chandragupta Pataliputra, and the Greeks called Sandrokotos, was, by his father's side, a descendant of an ancient royal house of Northern India, but his mother had been of low caste, and consequently he was of the people too; but royal traditions were strong within him, and old customs would be purposely fostered in order to revive well-known forms as against the innovations introduced by the Greeks. After Seleukotos had been repulsed, he sent Megathenes as his ambassadar to Pataliputra, and it is mainly from fragments of his accounts that we derive outside knowledge of India and Indian ways. He reports that Sandrokotos dwelt practically isolated in his palace, surrounded by an inner guard of armed women. Vincent A. Smith says that the rajah's prime minister,

Chanakya, prescribed that "on getting up from bed, the king should be received by troops of women armed with bows." It was a tradition that under certain circumstances these women were at liberty to slay the king, and the slayer married his successor. This personal guard of the king attended him when he appeared in public. When he went hunting the guard of women was quite numerous, some riding in chariots, others mounted on horses and elephants, and all equipped with weapons as though they were going on a campaign.

Both the levee and the hunting retinue are very ancient institutions which are frequently referred to in native literature. Talboys Wheeler, in his account of ancient Indian plays, says that the first act of *Sakimtala* (written by Kalidasa about 56 B.C.) opens in a forest where the rajah appears in a chariot carrying bows and arrows and surrounded by women wearing garlands, but also armed with bows and arrows. Sir Richard Burton mentions that many native princes, especially those of Hyderabad and the Deccan, maintained female guards called *urdu-begani* or "camp captains." Then there is the well-known instance of Ranjeet Singh of Lahore, who had a bodyguard of Amazons, 150 strong, recruited from the loveliest girls he could procure from Cashmere, Persia, and the Punjab. They were richly dressed, armed with bows and arrows, and mounted on milk-white chargers. These were merely *troupe de parade*, but they represented the historic royal bodyguard of a past age. At Lucknow there was a strong guard of female sepoys kept within the palace precincts. The same custom prevailed at Hyderabad, as we have already said, down to the middle of the nineteenth century.

Travellers give us lively accounts of these female troops, gaudily uniformed in scarlet tunics, green trousers, and red cloth caps trimmed with gold lace and great green plumes. They carried muskets and swords, and paraded like other troops, apparently being officered by men. We hear more than once of their taking a sanguinary part in palace cabals and dynastic upheavals, queen-mothers leading reactionary factions to power by the aid of the women soldiers. Although small and slender, these Hyderabad damsels in war panoply were often mistaken for ordinary male sepoys by casual visitors to the palace, for they cultivated a man-like bearing. No doubt these armed women were connected with the safe-keeping of the harem; but for their origin we must go much farther back, and in this connection it should he remembered that the rajah of old was a sacred personage, a demigod. Thus the Ramayana, which appears to have been reduced to writing in the fifth century B.C., but was much older, recounts the adventures of Rama-Chandra, an incarnation of the god Vishnu, born to Dasaratha, King of Aysdha (Oude), himself a descendant of the sun god, who was grandson of the Creator, Brahma; while the ancestor of the Pandavas, the heroes of the more celebrated Maha Bharata, was Chandra, the moon god of Northern India. Now, this is particularly interesting; for though we have seen reference to an Amazonian colony in Ceylon, the earliest and most deliberate mention of such a phenomenon appears in the Maha Bharata. This, like the earlier Ramayana, was originally a collection of religious and dynastic ballads dating back, according to Mounstuart Elphinstone's calculations, to at least 1500 B.C., and telling of the great deeds of the house of Bharata, the rules of an Aryan race. Later, however, the Brahmins annotated and converted the great epic into one of their own sacred books, in which the religious and moral teachings are embodied, though much of the older Vedic and pre-Vedic customs still remain in the voluminous poem.

The story opens in the city of Hastinapur, north-east of modern Delhi, on the upper banks of the Ganges, and is largely concerned with the doings of the exiled Pandavas, the rightful princes, who are banished by their uncle owing to the intrigues of their aunt. Perhaps the chief hero is the youngest prince, Arjuna, who interests us especially because the Maha Bharata gives a detailed account of an Aswamedha, or horse sacrifice, organised by him. We will follow Talboys Wheeler's analysis as far as it concerns our present purpose. The Aswamedha was at once a religious rite and an empire challenge. A horse having been carefully selected by the rajah, elaborate ceremonies followed, and the challenge engraved on a metal plate being fastened on the horse's forehead, it was turned loose. For the space of a whole twelvemonths the horse was permitted to wander whither it would, followed closely by the rajah and his retainers. If the horse trespassed on an adjoining state, the reigning rajah had but two alternatives: to seize it and place it in his stables and offer battle in its defence, or he might capture the horse and return it to the roving rajah with all due submission, which was tantamount to an acknowledgment of vassalage. In such circumstances the horse would go far and wide, and if all went well, at the end of the year it was conducted back triumphantly to the capital, where, in the presence of the conquered or submissive rajahs, it was ceremoniously sacrificed to the gods, amidst plaudits and songs in praise of the wanderers.

In the Maha Bharata we are told that Rajah Arjuna, after performing many gallant deeds and various sacrifices, decided upon the Aswamedha. Leaving Hastinapur, the horse leads the party into many strange places and formidable adventures. In the fifth stage he enters a country inhabited by women only, ruled over by Rani Paraminta. Now, the custom of this country was for the women, who were very beautiful and belonged to the rhackshasis class, to receive men, entertain them kindly, and retain them by their sides by their artful wiles; but if the men remained over a month (and there was little hope of their escape from the vigilant guard), they were killed. And those women who had harboured them and were not with child committed *satti*. In this manner was the nation kept ever young. When Arjuna reached this country, or rather was led there by the sacred horse, he fell into great perplexity. Turning to his followers, he said, "This is a marvellous country that the horse has led us to. If we conquer these women, we shall obtain no credit thereby; but if we are conquered, our disgrace will be greater than can be conceived. Moreover, these women are of great strength, and whoever lives with them for a month is a dead man. They will now seize our horse, and we shall find it hard to stand against them." As they pondered deeply, oppressed by gloomy forebodings, a brilliant cavalcade appeared. The women warriors were of dazzling loveliness, all between fifteen and sixteen years of age, mounted on superb horses, gorgeously dressed and adorned with pearls round their necks and arms, while they carried bows in their hands, and quivers full of arrows hung from their waists. Promptly they seized upon the Aswamedha horse and conveyed it to the rani, who ordered it to be taken to her stables, there to be kept as an extra charger.

Then the rani sallied forth mounted on an elephant and surrounded by her cavalry. As the opposing forces met, Rani Paraminta cried out, "Oh, Arjuna, you who have triumphed over so many men, can you conquer me?" and so saying, she shot a single arrow with such sureness of aim and such strength that the men stood amazed. "I myself will take you prisoner. You must abandon this unprofitable Aswamedha sacrifice, become my slave, drink with me, and pass your time in pleasure." "Yet, oh, rani, if I remain, I die," answered Arjuna. "In either case you are helpless. If you resist me, you fall by my arrows; if you remain, you have to face the light of my eyes." Then Arjuna confessed himself conquered, for he felt himself in love, captivated by her skill and her beauty. But he appealed to her superior understanding: it was impossible for him before gods and men to abandon the Aswamedha sacrifice; once commenced, it must be persisted in while life remained. He would carry out his task; then, if she would go to Hastinapur, on his return he would marry her and find gallant husbands for all who accompanied her. To this the rani replied that she had intended to kill them all; however, that which the rajah had said pleased her. She was willing to return the horse, even to hasten off to Hastinapur and there await Arjuna's glorious return. So she departed, surrounded by her cavalry, with a vast array of elephants loaded with treasure in her train. Which was, of course, an act of submission in accordance with the rules of this curious war game.

It is unnecessary to follow the adventurers through all their intricate windings to the happy ending, for our concern is with the women, but we may mention, as having a bearing on one aspect of our inquiry, that the horse took the wanderers to a forest where men and women grew on trees, flourishing for a day and then dying, and also to a land of serpent-worshippers. It is possible that this race of warrior women may have had some reference to the peculiar customs and warlike habits of the Nais women of the mountainous regions on the Malabar coast, though it seems to point to traditions of a peculiar state of affairs in some dim past. One point is to be noted: unlike the Greeks, who held their wars against the Amazons as amongst their most splendid feats of arms, the Indian prince holds quite another view, although he dreads both their strength and their snares. Probably the Brahmins have moralised the tale, with a view to show that the prince only escaped disaster by resisting allurements and bringing the adventure within religious bounds.

Both the Ramayana and the Maha Bharata describe India as a land where towns were few and far between, a land mostly covered with dense forests, inhabited chiefly by two classes of folk—the ascetics, who dwelt in seclusion, piling up treasures of power by prayer, observing austerities, and offering sacrifices; and by evil beings, who opposed holy hermits, dealt in magic, and were mostly cannibals. Many of the latter were women of the rhackshasis class, against whom Rama and Arjuna offer frequent battle.

Palladius, Bishop of Hellenopolis, in his *De Gentibus Indiæ*, writes of another order of affairs, for he says that the Brahmin men in the valley of the Ganges lived on one side of the river and the women on the other, the husbands visiting their wives for forty days in June, July, and August, but that when a child was born the husband never returned. Here, again, we seem to have a garbled rendering of the two phenomena, the long absence of men from their villages during seasons of work, and the segregation of the sexes during certain periods not altogether unconnected with physiological reasons and religious observances resulting therefrom.

Of the state where men were ruled over by women we have a hint from Hiuen Tsang, who says that on the northern borders of the Bramaputra he found the kingdom of Kin-chi ("of the golden family"), which was governed by a queen. Her husband was named king, but he did not rule. We are not told whether this was customary, or merely an accident due to a weak consort mated to a domineering rani, but the Chinese philosopher rather conveys the idea that this was the normal condition of affairs.

FRAGMENTS FROM MONSOLUS FRIEZE
(BRITISH MUSEUM).

Facing page 80.]

We hear of Amazonian isles much farther east. In the *Arabian Nights* the story of Hsan el Bassorah tells of his love for a beautiful and mysterious lady, who after their marriage and birth of children flies off to the island of Wak-Wak, thus having some analogy with the charming Lilith, according to the Talmudists Adam's first wife, who, having peopled the earth with devils, flew away to mate with Satan and beget the whole legion of jinns.[1] Hasan's wife, we are told, was the daughter of a very great king, who ruled over men and jinns. He had an army, 25,000 strong, of women, "smiters with swords and lungers with lances," any one of whom when mounted on a swift steed was equal in valour to a thousand knights. This king had seven daughters, who were braver and more expert than their 25,000 "sisters." The eldest of these seven, who "in valour and horsemanship, and craft and skill, and magic excels all folk of her dominions," was Hasan's wife and queen of Wak-Wak, the furthermost of a series of seven isles, whereon there was a forest near unto Mount Wak, where the trees bore fruit with the faces of the sons of Adam, who cried, "Wak-wak, glory to the Creating King," as soon as the sun rose, and again, "Wak-wak, glory to God," with the setting of the sun.

Lane in his notes to his translation says that the island of Wak-Wak, or El-Wak-Wak, well known in tradition and chronicles, appeared to be near Borneo. It was a land governed by a queen

[1] This was, no doubt, an attempt on the part of the Talmudists to account for the worship of demons by the early Hebrews.

surrounded by troops of beautiful women. Gold was abundant, and the trees brought forth women, who hung by their hair from the branches, crying "Wak-wak," and when their hair was cut they died! An Arab author, Ibn-el-Wardee, quoted by Lane, mentions an island of women in the same sea in which there were no men. Mendoza, the historian of China, heard of two islands, a male and a female, like those of Marco Polo, off the coast of Japan; and it is curious that Professor de Goeje, as Sir Richard Burton informs us, heard Japan spoken of in Canton as Wo-Kwok. Burton in his notes on the tale of Hasan holds that the Arabian geographers spoke of two Wak-Waks. He quotes the French translation of Ibn-el-Fakih and Al-Ma'udi, who locate one of the islands in East Africa beyond Zanzibar and Sofala.

On the other hand: "Le territoire des Zendjs commence au canal (Al-Khali) derive du Haut Nil et se prolonge jusqu'au pays des Sofalah et des Wak-Wak.' Which Burton says is simply the peninsula of Guardefui, conquered by the Gallas before the Moslem Somals swept them away. The pagan Gallas continually called out "Wak" like the Moslems cry "Allah"! "This identification," continues Burton, "explains a host of other myths, such as the Amazons who, as Marco Polo tells us, held the Female Island. The fruit, which resembled a woman's head (whence the puellæ wakwakieness hanging by their hair from trees) and which when ripe called out 'Wak-wak' and 'Allah al Khallak' (the Creator), refers to the calabash trees, that grotesque growth, a vegetable elephant, whose gourds, something larger than a man's head, hang by a slender filament." The second Wak-Wak has been variously identified with the Seychelles, Madagascar, Malacca, Sunda, Java, an island off Sumatra, an island off the coast of Japan, and even far-off New Guinea, the latter because there flocks of birds of paradise settle on the trees and call out "Wak-wak-wak." Other authorities tell us that to the south of China there was a maleless island, where the women mated with the winds; while the patriarch Bermudes refers to an island in those waters inhabited by Amazons, who, in the usual way, only received men at stated seasons, keeping the girls born to them and sending the boys to their fathers. Then, as Pinkerton tells us, the Jesuit missionaries heard of similar islands from inhabitants of the Marianne Island, these rumours referring to one of the same group, the Ladronnes of evil repute, or to the more southerly Carolines, of which like tales were told. So vague, however, was all this, that it may with equal possibility apply to one fabled isle, floating in indefinite seas, roaming now here, now there, according to man's credulity and ignorance, or to certain abnormal social conditions cropping up again and again in many localities, far apart on the face of the waters as well as in time. And this brings us back to the Far East.

Certainly in this Farthest East not only the tradltions, but the actual existence of Amazon guards may be traced to within our own times. In the early seventies of the last century there were women palace-guards at Bangkok, on the same lines as those at

Hyderabad. And at the same period in Bantam, which then held an almost semi-independent position under the Dutch, the king had a royal troop of women soldiers, who rode astride and carried muskets and lances. It was said that if the king died without a direct heir, the Amazons met and elected a king from among their own sons. Sir Richard Burton points out that Tien-Wang, the Celestial King of the Tae-Pings ("Princes of Peace"), had a bodyguard of 1000 women soldiers. Now this is particularly interesting, because Tien-Wang had headed a formidable rebellion against the reactionary Tartar Emperor of China in 1851, and calling himself Tien-Teh (Celestial Virtue), declared that he was the restorer of the true God, second son of God, brother of Jesus, sovereign of all beneath the sky, true lord of China. This universal monarch and his misnamed followers accomplished great conquests, and would probably have made themselves masters of China had not Gordon intervened, bringing about defeats and the capture of Nankin in 1864, whereupon Tien-Wang committed *hari-kari*. His followers for the most part escaped into Tonkin, where they were long known as the very troublesome Black Banners and Yellow Banners. The momentous point in all this is the dual claim to sovereignty made by Tien-Wang, as a divine personage and a world-monarch, and his surrounding himself with female guards, which connects the Chinese religious reformer sociologically not only with the princes of the Deccan, but, as we shall presently see, with the dusky rulers of the Upper Nile and the west coast of Africa.

SECTION OF MONSOLUS FRIEZE, COMBAT OF GREEKS AND AMAZONS. BRITISH MUSEUM.

Facing page 85.]

CHAPTER V

Modern Amazons of the Caucasus

From age to age memories of the Amazons persistently clung to the Pontus, to the whole of the Caucasian range of mountains and the regions immediately beyond, or those coming within their influenee. Many writers held that some sections of the broken Themysciran state had after the debacle taken refuge among the higher mountains, and there, in security if not in solitude, carried, more or less in its entirety, the traditional mode of life. To give colour to this there were the generally prevailing reports of fighting women in those regions. When Mithridates v., King of Pontus, made war on the Roman colonies in Asia Minor, between 100 and 98 B.C., he had in his vast army strong bodies of auxiliaries from Scythia and Sarmatia, who were looked upon as barbarians both by friend and foe. After the battles, it is said, the Romans found among the heaps of slain women clothed in armour and with arms in their hands. Appianus the historian, in his account of this war, touches upon the matter and raises the interesting question whether the term was not already becoming generalised. According to him: "There were found among the prisoners and the hostages several women whose wounds were as great and dangerous as those of the men. These women were said to be Amazons, either because the auxiliary troops belonged to nations neighbouring on Amazonia, or because the barbarians gave that name to all warlike women."

More than three centuries later the traditions and habits still lingered on hereabouts. Gibbon tells us that in the theatrically gorgeous procession on the occasion of the Emperor Aurelian's triumph in 274 A.D., there marched ten heroines of the Gothic nation, taken in arms, and exhibited to the Roman populace as "Amazons." It is in recording this fact that the great sceptic wrote, like Appianus, with remarkable hesitancy: "It is *almost* impossible that a society of Amazons should ever have existed in the Old or New World." From such a quarter we might well have looked for more downright utterance. There was, however, enough of mystery to justify caution, even to the extent of the un-Gibbon-like italics.

For instance, Jacob Reineggs, in a description of the Caucasus written in 1796, says that the Circassians in his day declared that before their own forefathers had come to the Black Sea, the land was in the possession of the "emmetsh," with whom they were at war. The women "admitted no men among them, but, full of warlike spirit, associated with themselves any women who cared to share their wanderings and to join their heroic guild." Which seems to describe a nomadic tribe composed of the flotsam and jetsam of social wreckage in this veritable cockpit of conflicting races. Schober, in his account of Asiatic Russia, places the women farther afield, for he heard rumours that the "Emazuhn" still inhabited the mountains of

Great Tartary, and though they in his day, it seems, no longer indulged in constant fighting, they were accomplished hunters, and kept their husbands in a condition of subserviency. On the other hand, we are told that the Kalmuks, an Asiatic Russian tribe of Mongol extraction, and therefore possibly acquainted with the Emazuhn of whom Schober speaks, applied the term "aëmetzaine" to strong women full of vigour. Whether the word was philologically and intentionally descriptive we are not informed. It may have been derivative, a later corruption of the Greek or, more correctly speaking, Greecised term amazon; in fact, the name of a type may have been applied to an individual, as seems to have been done in the days of Mithridates. In any case, the long persistence of a word in a special locality, varying slightly though it does, and applying to a particular race or to a type of women, cannot lightly be set aside. It may mean merely the survival of a legend, but may also indicate that there is some justification for the legend-makers, and this the local history seems to confirm.

At all events, rumours of this kind repeated by travellers in or writers dealing with these regions from the Middle Ages down to quite the end of the eighteenth century certainly point in such a direction. Sir John Mandeville, who looms large in the company of the quaint raconteurs, wrote of the Amazons as of an existing nation in his day, and says, among a plethora of other things, that they kept the lost ten tribes of Israel shut up in a valley surrounded by mountains. It must have been pretty obvious even to the credulous knight that there were serious gaps in those chains of mountains, and that the vigilance of the good women was far from being above reproach, since the Amazonian *coralle* had not perceptibly checked the wandering propensities of the Hebrews. For there were, even in those days, opposing camps, who placed the lost tribes in Abyssinia and others on the banks of the Ganges, a confusion probably due to the haziness prevailing among the mediæval geographers, but also suggested by racial peculiarities in those distant lands. But it is interesting to find the Nestorians of Mesopotamia claiming that they represent the lost tribes, while the Jews of the Caucasus have always persisted that they were descendants of the ten tribes, those of Georgia holding that they were taken prisoner by Nebuchadnezzar, and those from other districts declaring that they were carried away from Palestine by Shalmaneser. All of which points to the singular mixing of races hereabouts, while the connection of the women with the lost tribes also has its significance. The Amazons were Scythians, and, as we know, one of the most persistent of the traditions concerning these matters is that the Scythians (those forefathers of the whole Teutonic family, and consequently of the Angle and the Saxon) were the true representatives of the lost ten tribes. Remembering the old forms of worship among the Jews and their later backsliding devotion to Ashtoreth, Queen of the Heavens, and that among the scattered remnants of old tribes the Cabala, or traditional lore, would prevail over the written law, and no doubt give rise to certain of the mystic extravagances that arose elsewhere, its secrets kept alive by an elect band of initiated, we see here again an association of the armed women guards with religious ritual.

Many as are the questions that a perusal of Mandeville's tale raises, a much more reliable author, John Cartwright, who had travelled extensively in the East and wrote an account of his experiences in 1603, speaks of Armenia with its great plains encompassed by rows of mountains, those spurs of the Taurus and Caucasus ranges. The people he found to be "industrious in all kinds of labour," and then he adds, as though by way of contrast: "their women very skilful and active in shooting and managing any sort of weapon, like the fierce Amazons in antique times and the women at this day which inhabit the Mountain Xatach in Persia." This reminds us irresistibly of Herodotus's remarks on the Sauromatœ. Then that adventurous character, Sir John Chardin, who, beginning life as plain Jean Chardin, son of a Paris jeweller, enjoyed a most picturesque career in the East, and ended his days peacefully in England as a protégé of Charles II., says that when he was in Georgia in 1671 the Amazons had only recently invaded an outlying position of the kingdom somewhere to the north-west. From what he says it would seem to have been a tribe similar to that referred to by Hippocrates when he declares that a body of Scythians dwelt immediately to the north of the Palus Mæotis, which sea he places entirely in Europe. Their women, says the great physician, were red, rode astride on horseback, using the bow and arrow even when riding at full speed, went to war, and did not marry until they had killed three men; so that it was only natural that the Greeks should call them Androchtones. When they had garnered the three masculine scalps, these amiable girls gave up warfare and hunting, to settle down to a quiet married life. They seared their right breasts with red-hot irons, and as a consequence their right arms grew exceptionally powerful. Which account affords another interesting link connecting the Themysciran women, the Sauromatœ females of man-like habits described by Herodotus, the Sauromatœ Gynœcocratumeni of Pliny, and the modern feminine warriors of these savage parts.

As for Chardin, he confesses that he had not seen the Amazonian country, which he considered formed part of Tartary, but while in Georgia he heard much about it and its inhabitants, and was even shown the woollen costume of peculiar cut belonging to a big woman, which was said to have been taken from an Amazon killed in the late wars. Discussing the whole subject with the young Prince of Georgia, they agreed that there was nothing improbable in the stories about women fighting on horseback. Women warriors, and nations governed by aggressive queens, were too well known in those parts to give rise to much astonishment; and as for riding, most of the maids and matrons were good horsewomen, and they always rode astride like men. The prince was of opinion that the recent invaders must have been nomadic Scythians, but he did not appear to have heard of the Greek traditions.

Indeed, this phenomenon of fighting women was widespread, extending through Armenia and the Kurd country to Syria and parts of Arabia, as well as north of the Sea of Azof and eastward into Tartary. Of the southerly Amazonian females we hear constantly in connection with the conquests of Mahomet's early successors. Ockley tells us that at the first siege of Damascus the Moslem women who were guarding the camp of invaders were captured, and insulting terms proffered to them by the Greeks. But the women, being encouraged by two Hamzarite companions, supposed to be descendants of the Amalekites, resistance was at once organised. Arming themselves with tent-poles, and forming a close ring, they kept the enemy at bay, breaking the skulls or limbs of any who advanced too near. Even mounted men could make no impression, for the tent-poles were longer than lances, and easily broke the horses' legs, bringing steed and cavalier to the ground. The fight was gallantly kept up until the Moslem horsemen came galloping up to the relief, and then the women helped their own troops in following up and routing the discomfited Greeks. So ended this affair: but it is evident that had they not been relieved, they might well have made their escape in the darkness; and had their own friends been slaughtered, could have wandered off to sheltering hills, and there formed a women's community.

Then we have an incident of a different kind at the second siege, when one of the Arab leaders was brought into camp mortally wounded by a poisoned arrow. His wife, a daughter of the Himiar tribe, seized his bow and arrows, and sallying forth, joined in the battle, and succeeded in putting out an eye of the noble Thomas, the Greek Governor of Damascus. Still she continued her onslaught, fighting all day, and venturing so far in the fray under the walls that, her darts exhausted, she was captured during a sortie, but subsequently rescued. Again and again she proved a rallying-point to the besiegers. Such actions were of constant occurrence, both on the side of the attacking forces and the attacked, but they caused little surprise, for these bold creatures were "accustomed from their youth to mount the horse, ply the bow, and launch the javelin." And much the same was said of the tribes to the north.

Probably the most circumstantial account of the late survivals in the Caucasian regions is given by Father Angelo Lamberti in his careful *Relation de la Colchide*, published in 1654, as the result of his long stay in the country. The good priest declines to discuss the whole question of an Amazon state or race, but says that when he was in Mingrelia the king of that country was notified that a large body of troops had left the Caucasus, and splitting up into three divisions, one party went into Muscovy, and the other two set about attacking local tribes. They were beaten off, and among the dead were found a great number of women, who had taken an active part in the fighting. They were all in armour, which was beautifully wrought and decorated with a true feminine love of elegance. This armour comprised helmets, breastplates, jambieres, cuissards, etc., all constructed of iron plates so skilfully put together that the wearers retained perfect freedom of movement. Attached to the breastplates were short skirts of woollen material dyed a bright red. Their half-boots were ornamented with brass discs strung on threads of exquisitely plaited goats' hair. The women carried bows and arrows, the latter having long gilded shafts, the heads being of iron, not pointed or barbed in the usual style, but in the form of a sharp cutting edge, like the blade of a knife or a pair of scissors. Their cutting edge was placed at right angles to the shaft. These must, therefore, have been only short-flight darts, intended for

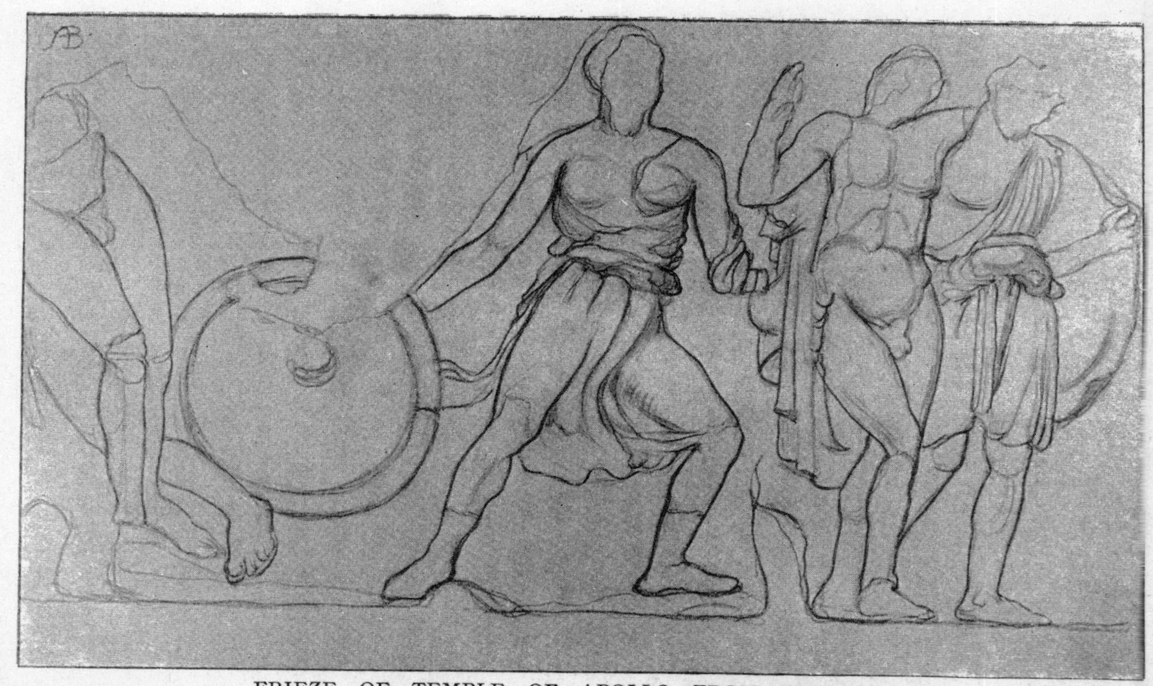

FRIEZE OF TEMPLE OF APOLLO FROM PHIGALEIA.

Facing page 92.]

use at close quarters, and having a severing or slashing rather than a piercing action. This form of the arrow-head is so extraordinary that it is rather suggestive of a modified form of the crescent-headed arrow, so much heard of in the East as a mystic weapon of great power.

Rama, the demigod-hero of the Ramayana, did wonderful deeds with his irresistible crescent-shaped arrows. So did Rajah Arjuna, as related to us in the Maha Bharata. It is true that the latter lost his life through one of these, but it was the only weapon that caused him harm. It was shot, too, by his own son, the rajah who dwelt in a magnificent palace encircled by walls of gold in the city of Manipur, itself walled about by battlemented ramparts of silver. He was a man who had converse with diverse dealers in magic, such as the King of Serpents. When he sped the sacred arrow in anger against his unknown father, it severed Arjuna's head, which, however, was subsequently reunited to the body, and life restored, thanks to the jewel borrowed from the King of Serpents. In all these cases the crescent arrows were sacred weapons. Indeed, this form of the dart was symbolical, and was used in sacrifices by the large following of lunar deities in the East. Sin, the second of the great Babylonian gods, was a moon god, and his terrible daughter, Ishtar, wore the crescent as her symbol. And, as we know, there were sanctuaries to moon gods in the fastnesses of the Caucasus, where human sacrifices were offered even in late days. Thus it looks as though the weapons described by Father Lamberti were actually survivals in a degraded form. Lamberti says that various pieces of armour and feminine gear were brought in, but apparently the king's offer of a handsome reward to any one who would bring him a real live Amazon proved ineffective. Nevertheless, it is said that the women were constantly at war with the Kalmuks, who, as we have seen, respected their valour and called them aëmetzaines.

These rumours continued quite late, and even in the middle of the nineteenth century we hear of fighting women. A notable instance is that of a kind of modern Thalestris, a certain Kurdish chieftainess known as the "Black Virgin," who at the opening of the Crimean War headed a body of 1000 cavalry, and having paraded before the Sultan's palace at Constantinople, went off to fight under Omar Pasha against the Russians on the Danube.

CHAPTER VI

Amazons of Europe

In order, on the one hand, to round off their stories of the break-up of the great Amazonian power, and on the other, to account for certain phenomena witnessed in various corners of the then known world, the Greek chroniclers put forward various plausible tales. While, as we have seen, they asserted that a galley-load or two of female prisoners, being conveyed to Greece after the battle of the Thermodon, revolted, and making their way beyond the Tanais, founded the Sarmatian-Amazon state, so, they held, the routed legions of Orithya, smarting under their defeat before Athens, and deciding never to return to Themyscira, wandered through Thrace into the wilds of Central Europe. Of these women there are many to claim descent. Indeed, Gilbert Charles le Gendre, Marquis de Saint Aubin-sur-Loire, writing in the early part of the eighteenth century in his *Antiquités Française*, declares that the Franks had sprung from the Thracian Amazons. Other sections of the lost legions are supposed to have lingered for many centuries in more or less autonomous colonies in various secluded corners.

Curious tales of these "women nations" crept up unexpectedly in popular lore. This was, no doubt, due to the Sarmatians and their customs, those descendants of the Sauromatœ of Herodotus and Pliny. In his *Natural History* Pliny says that beyond—that is, to the north-east of—the river Tanais, there dwelt the Sauromatœ Gynœcocratumeni ("the Sauromatœ ruled over by women"). This would seem to point to a matriarchal form of government rather than to the old Amazonian manless state, and was, in fact, an elaboration of Herodotus, whose account of the Sauromatœ we have already given at some length. It will be remembered that this nation was said to be a colony founded by part of the Amazons whom Hercules had dispatched towards Greece, but who, all too insecurely guarded, had risen in revolt and directed their galleys to the Black Sea coast. The rule of a queen was quite within the laws of the old Slav race, and we have in Pliny's story little more than a confusion between a queen's dominions and a mythical matriarchate. We may even take note of the views of some authorities who hold that the "ruled over by women" must not be taken too literally, but rather be regarded in the light of a descriptive jibe addressed by neighbouring women-enslaving races against the Sarmatians, who admitted women to share their most prized privileges, sports and warfare.

The geography of this region is very confused, not only because the boundary between Europe and Asia has been a constantly shifting line, but owing to the still more bewildering fact of natural topographical transformations. Inland seas have shrunk, rivers changed their courses, swamps dried up. As for the Tanais, it was regarded as the boundary between Europe and Asia, and has been identified

SECTION OF PHIGALEIAN FRIEZE, COMBAT OF GREEKS AND AMAZONS. BRITISH MUSEUM.

Facing page 97.]

with the Don, which river rises in Lake Ivan Ozero in the far government of Tula, flows south-east, then south-west, and so into the Sea of Azof (the old Palus Mæotis, once far more eastward than it is now). Some geographers have identified the Tanais with the Donetz, which flows south-east from a little above Karkof and joins the Don not far above the Sea of Azof, but this seems quite improbable. As regards the Sarmatians, it is clear that they migrated westward, being the first Slavs to spread over Russia, Poland, and Bohemia, and this accounts for much in the survival of both legends and habits.

As late as the eighteenth century we hear of women communities in Russia: indirectly from George, Lord Macartney, who went on a delicate mission as British Ambassador to St. Petersburg between the years 1765 and 1767. Writing upon the subject of the Cossacks, he refers to those of Zaporavia, who, he says, were 30,000 strong, and "consist of persons of all nations, and live in a singular sort of society, to which no woman is admitted. They are a sort of male Amazons, who, at a particular season of the year, resort to a certain island of the Dnieper, and in the neighbourhood, where they rendezvous with the women dependent upon them." He says their customs were those of the most primitive savagery. The girls remained with their mothers, but the boys, on reaching a suitable age, accompanied the men, to be trained as hunters and warriors. This arrangement, however, was far more natural under the circumstances than appeared to the worthy Irishman, whose details as to the mode of life and excesses need not be taken too seriously, for they appear to be the usual gloss placed by superior ignorance on exceptional customs only partially understood. What stands out clearly enough is that these men, under the service which they owed to the Government, had perforce to lead a nomadic life, and the organisation of these warrior bands compelled them, while away patrolling vast stretches of country, busy training and hunting, to leave their womenkind in village camps. No doubt a river island would be chosen as a place of some safety, having a natural protection, and this would give rise to the wild legends. However, the student will find the passage in all its crudeness given in *Some Account of the Life of Earl Macartney*, edited by Sir J. Barlow.

As we have said, rumours of such colonies spread far afield. Long before Lord Macartney had penned his description of the Zaporavian Cossacks, Adamus Bremensis, writing in the sixteenth century, declared that there existed an island peopled by women only, lying off the Baltic shores. It is true, however, that this is generally said to be an error of the learned and pious historian, who confused the term Gwenland (Finland) with the land of gwens (the land of women).

That women in Europe as elsewhere took up arms in defence of their homes against external oppression, or during internecine disorders, there are endless instances to prove, from the days of Roman expansion down to our own times. With us in England, there have been many notable women leaders, and not a few examples of women banding together for warlike purposes, though sometimes without bloodthirstiness. One such case may be classed with the innocent stratagem of the Quaker, not he who trusted in Providence and kept his powder dry, but that other, who, more fundamentally pacific, indulged in dummy wooden cannon, only formidable to look upon. When the French, under the inspiration of the "Corsican Ogre," made their forlorn attempts to invade these islands, turning their attention to the west, Ireland and Wales, our countrywomen aided and abetted our men volunteers in many defensive ways. At Fishguard a notable feint was adopted on the approach of the enemy, the women banding together, with red shawls about their shoulders, marched about and massed in solid battalions on the green hillsides, so that the French general was deceived into believing that large bodies of reinforcements were at hand, with the result that the landing was not pressed. Local tradition has it that one of the red-shawled women, Jemima Nicholas, whose modest tombstone is still to be seen in the churchyard, actually managed to corner and deliver to the authorities seven French soldiers.

So naturally do particular needs bring about similar results that we find a parallel to this in Spanish history during the heroic period of the Gothic struggle against the Moorish invasion. One of the leaders, beaten back from the coast to his fortified town of Tadmir, found his fighting ranks so seriously depleted by the sword that he caused the women to don male attire, tie their hair under their chins to represent whiskers and beards, take up arms, and form a background to the actual fighters.

Thus strengthened he was able to present a redoubtable front to the Moslem and thereby exact honourable terms, which were scrupulously observed, in spite of the deception.

The true fighting spirit appears to have always been strong within the Spanish women's breasts. During the War of Succession, Barcelona was long defended largely by its women, though it ultimately fell to Marshal Berwick. Then during the Napoleonic campaign, when Saragossa was attacked by Marshal Lefrebre, there were only 120 soldiers and a few old guns to defend its 12-feet high ramparts. So the women formed themselves into companies of 200 and 300 strong, relieving the men and fighting side by side with them. Lefrebre could make no impression until he succeeded by means of bribery in having the powder magazine blown up. Then he rushed in with his troops, taking advantage of the dismay and disorganisation; but one of the maids, Agostina, seizing a lighted match, discharged a cannon at the serried ranks of the invaders, and rallying the town garrison, expelled the French, keeping them at a distance until the British came hurrying to the rescue. Agostina begged to be allowed to retain her rank as an artilleryman. She was awarded a pension and the honour of bearing the name and arms of Saragossa. On the Ligurian coast we hear of many equally brave actions on the part of women in keeping the Saracens at bay. A later incident, when the Niçois came into conflict with the Barbaresco pirates, is worthy of note. It occurred as late as 1527, when Catherine Sigurana was the means of repulsing

Barbarossa from the citadel of Nice. Barbarossa, Bey of Tunis, was the vassal of Suliman II., the abhorrent ally of the shameless Francis I. of France. Sigurana was a patriotic virago of a type different to Penthesilea, for she was nicknamed Maufacia, which tells its own sad tale. But, indeed, every country in Europe had its fighting women and its individual feminine warriors, even the spirit of aggression having been kindled among crowds of them, as in the abortive prelude to the first Crusade, when Peter the Hermit led his contingent of 40,000 men, women, and children to destruction.

Not one of these well-known warlike acts of women, mainly in defence of their homes, was associated with any form of, or claim to, women rule. There is, however, one episode in European history which does stand out with peculiar prominence in spite of its semi-fabulous embellishments; and there is a second semi-Amazonian passage which is only too authentic.

Bohemia, the Boiemum of Tacitus, originally formed part of the vast Hercynian forest. It is an elevated plateau, practically surrounded by a chain of high and grim mountains, whose spurs jut out into the plain, and is traversed by many rivers, including the romantic Elbe. Here the Borii, a Celtic people, dwelt before the advent of the Marcomani, who in turn gave place to the Slavs, themselves of the Sarmatian stock, and, therefore, presumably connected with tribes having Amazonian tendencies. These Slavs of Bohemia were ruled over by elected chiefs, the last of whom was Crocus, or Krok, who had a daughter named Libussa.

Æneas Silvius, in his *Historia Boëmii*, says that Libussa succeeded her father, and calling many women to high office, trained her sex assiduously in military exercises before leading them to numerous victories. On her death there were those in the kingdom who desired to bring about a change in this state of affairs, which caused a revolt of the women, headed by Valasca, or Dlasta, one of Libussa's favourite henchwomen. Valasca seized the reins of government, placing women in all offices. She ordained that only women should be trained to the art of warfare. The better to ensure this end, while the girls were to receive a specialised military education, the boys were to be so treated as to render this impossible, their right eye and their thumbs being removed, making the handling of weapons in a fight out of the question—a piece of cruelty which betrayed the inherent weakness of her schemes and cause. Valasca is said to have reigned for seven strenuous years, and then on her demise the business of the nation resumed its normal course. Great ruins on Mount Vidovole, known as the Divin-hrad ("The Virgin's City"), were long pointed out as the reputed headquarters of Valasca.

That these experiments in high statecraft were not without a patriotic basis, and tended to foster national pride, is proved by the fact that the old folk-songs are full of allusion to valiant deeds of these two heroines. These time-worn fragments of pagan civilisation are intensely interesting, for they show that the whole mode of thought of the people tended to self-glorification, the whole tribe forming one large family, and their outlook on the world was animistic. Nature was in close sympathy with the chosen people. A squabble among petty chiefs over land questions sufficed to cause the rivers to overflow and the mountains to quake. It was on such a nation that Libussa and Valasca tried their powers. But, as is the way with minstrelsy, the deeds of the good women and the effects that they produced were somewhat exaggerated. The truth seems to be that Libussa, the youngest of three daughters, was born in 680, succeeded her father in 700, and died in 738, leaving heirs. It was strictly within the primitive Slav habits that a younger child, if possessing special qualifications, should succeed to family property and headship; for, with sound common sense, primogeniture was not recognised, practical experience so constantly demonstrating the first-born as deficient, mentally and physically. Libussa, who was reported to possess the gift of prophecy, called to her assistance her two sisters, Kaça and Teta, and also instituted for her support a Council of Virgins. Among other of her works was the establishment of the Three Orders, or Estates, partly as a barrier against the pretensions of the nobles, and partly to maintain the old laws, for the Orders acted as Courts of Justice. She married Przemyl, a peasant, founded the city of Prague, and wherever possible employed women to fill responsible posts. At her death, however, the Council of Virgins was abolished. Thereupon Valasca, Libussa's chief confidante, rose, and gathering the discontented about her, attempted to found a women's state; but her triumph was only partial and shortlived. One can well imagine that the edicts issued by a select committee of "young persons" must have been decidedly irksome to the staunch men of the somewhat turbulent and much-threatened land, so that the overthrow of the feminine influence set up by Libussa cannot be a subject for much wonderment. Still, Bohemia, even in her days, was very far from being an Amazonia. Libussa herself married and left a posterity which was represented in the proud house of the Hapsburgs, whose last descendant in the direct line, Maria Theresa, played so important a part in Europe, and did so much for her country. That the old folk-songs and traditions have in the main transmitted faithfully enough certain extreme proposals of the irate Valasca (ironic Fate's caricature of her worthy mistress) is probable. However, as, apparently, the majority of the men preserved their right eye and their thumbs, they could afford, after the heat of the struggle, to sing only of the glorious achievements of the safely dead heroines.

The second series of episodes do not reflect much honour on humanity, or rather, carry us back to the primitive stage of the Greek mythus, though certain mitigating circumstances have to be taken into consideration. Quite early in the days of the first French Revolution the women, especially those of Paris, assumed an active share in political affairs, and rarely, it must be confessed, took sides in the interests of peace or goodwill. But, as Michelet truly observes, the women had for centuries borne the brunt of double suffering, for they partook of the miseries of those they loved as well as of their own. They were driven to desperation by a long and heavy accumulation of wrongs, which seemed to have no ending. They had taken part in the capture of the Bastille, and had witnessed attempts at reaction, tolerated if not encouraged by the Royal Family, and fostered by the Court ladies.

Maddened by tales of how the national tricolour cockade had been trampled underfoot by the courtiers in the presence of the king and queen, and replaced by the "anti-patriotic" black or white bunch of ribbons, that momentous march on Versailles was decided on. A young girl at the Central Markets had seized a drum and beaten the general assembly, and as the crowd of women poured forth they were met by others from the Faubourg Saint-Antoine, and contingents of yet others who had been harangued in the Palais Royal by a young lady. Another woman, the already notorious actress, Theroigne de Mericourt, surnamed "the Amazon of Liege," grasping a lighted match, got astride of a cannon, and was dragged along thus in the hurly-burly of that curious procession, half friendly, half ferocious, almost wholly demented, wending its weary way to aristocratic and unspeakably profligate Versailles. The women would not be denied, and they, more than the men, were instrumental in bringing king and queen, dauphin and the rest, back to the Tuileries, that gigantic stride towards the tragic end. Early in 1792 the Municipality of Paris had decided that all sansculottes should be armed with pikes, and in August of that year the National Assembly decreed that the ordinance should apply to every citizen; whereupon the women claimed that they too came under the law. It was in the spirit of the "Declaration of the Rights of Women," issued by Olympe de Gonges as a counterpoise of the *Contrat Social* of Jean Jacques Rousseau and the "Declaration of the Rights of Man," in which she declared, "Woman is born free and with equal rights with man. Woman has the right to mount the scaffold: she must also have the right to mount the platform of the orator."

At last the market-women, those robust Dames de la Halle, and their sisters of the Faubourg Saint-Antoine, formed themselves into an Amazonian brigade, imposing on themselves the duty of guarding the prisoners, escorting the dismal *tomberaux* to the guillotine on the Place de la Révolution. Their uniform was a short skirt, striped blue, white, and red; sabots covered their feet; and they wore the red Phrygian cap (the "Cap of Liberty," formally adopted as a badge by the Jacobins in 1792), adorned with a huge tricolour cockade. Each woman had a baldric slung across her shoulder, supporting a cutlass, and carried the democratic pike. It was an ugly band, often engaged in uglier work. Theroigne de Mericourt and Rose Lacombe had come to the fore in most of these events. Theroigne, indeed, was placed in command of the third corps of the army of the Faubourg, and went about dressed in a red riding-habit, huge hat and plume of feathers, and carrying a sword of honour that had been presented to her. Another warrior, the opera-singer, la Maillard, who had represented the Goddess of Freedom at the Feast of Reason, adopted a different outward manifestation of "the rights of women," donning male attire, fighting duels, and, assisted by other similarly attired women, went about Paris endeavouring to compel every maid and matron to follow suit.[1] All these women came to grief. Theroigne, suspected of being a Girondist by the Amazons, was seized on the Terrace of the Tuileries, stripped naked, and whipped like a naughty child by her erstwhile companions in arms, amidst the hilarious jeers of the populace. She became a raving lunatic, and died in Bicétre as late as 1817. Rose Lacombe came to her undoing through love: trying to save an aristocrat, she fell into disgrace; but, although toppled from her dizzy position as popular favourite, she was luckier than her companion leader, dying in peace long after the revolutionary fury had run its course. Olympe de Gonges, having irritated Robespierre by her pretensions and irresponsibility, was condemned to die; and though she pleaded approaching maternity, a jury of matrons consigned her to the guillotine; while la Maillard, by her endeavour to force her sisters into pantaloons, raised such a tumult that she hurried the Committee of Public Safety into issuing a decree that women should take no part in government, and that all their clubs where politics were discussed should be closed.

Less shocking to human feelings, though equally warlike in spirit, were the armed battalions of women and girls formed in the provinces, especially in the Dauphiné, who were sworn to defend the country and

[1] Similar sartorial eccentricities have shown themselves in our days. There are followers of la Maillard and also of Theroigne, for the colour manifestation is showing itself among the "advanced" women of Finland. Mr. Paul Waineman says: "Red is now the recognised hue for women socialists. This is carried to such an extent that the female socialist members of the Diet wear bright scarlet gowns when sitting in the House."

democracy. They were also active in the clubs and political circles ; and on the other hand, the women of the Royalist or reactionary side entered the militant ranks : there were various leaders and individual fighters, though few instances of their banding together in companies. But the feminine ambition of the French women in those days was to share work and responsibilities, not to usurp independent power.

CHAPTER VII

Amazons of Africa

Diodorus Siculus, quoting Dionysius the historian, says that there was a prodigious race of Amazons who rose, flourished exceedingly, and disappeared long before the Trojan War—so long before, indeed, that their renown had been obscured by the newer glory of the Amazons of the Pontus. The more ancient race had its origin in Libya, that Africa which lay between Egypt and Ethiopia on the east, the Atlantic on the west, bounded on the north by the classic strip of Mediterranean shore, and on the south by the imaginary Oceanus River, a land harbouring many curious things and peoples. These regions, according to "ancient histories," unfortunately not cited, were at one time famed for their "warlike women of great force." Among these were the Gorgons, who dared to make war on the gods and the Greeks, and against whom Perseus, that prince of high virtue, son of Jupiter and foremost of Grecians of his day, fought under many difficulties and at much hazard to himself, so terrible were the women's valour and might. From which whole-hearted acceptance of the gorgonomachia we have fair warning to be cautious of these "ancient histories." Diodorus, it is interesting to note, writes of the Gorgons as of a numerous tribe or nation, rather than as the classic trio of sisters whom the gentle-eyed Pallas Athene and the aristocratic Perseus treated so scurvily. Certain it is that viragoes of the Gorgon type, setting divine and human law at defiance, have constantly made their appearance hereabout and a little to the southward. However, leaving this subject of inquiry aside, we find our authors stating that it was on the western limits of this land of strange things, "towards the uttermost parts of the earth," that the Amazons first sprang to fame. There they "led another manner of life than our women do, for they used to exercise themselves in feats of arms until a certain time for the conservation of their virginity, and after that was expired they married to have children. They alone held the dominion and commanded, administering all public offices and affairs, and their men, after the fashion of women, had in charge the private business of the house, obeying their wives, and utterly ignorant of matters of war and the government of the commonwealth." We have here, in this special form of marriage, a radical departure from the Themysciran policy, and one all the more striking as it coincides in a most remarkable manner with what is reported of African Amazons within historic times, as we shall have occasion to relate in connection with the eastern and western regions. In other particulars—in war training, suppression of the right breast, and special reliance on horse-craft—the African and Asiatic customs largely agreed.

As regards the first seat of their government, a most interesting question arises. Diodorus says that they lived on the island Hisperia, otherwise Tritonia, so called because it was situated in a fen called Tritonida from a river of that name which entered the ocean. The fen lay between Ethiopia and the Atlas. It is generally assumed that by this the Hesperides, or Fortunate Isles (or the modern Canaries), is intended, and this conjecture seems to be confirmed by the statement that Tritonia was a country subject to earthquakes and where, as it did in the Asiatic cradle of the Amazon race, flames belched forth from the ground. But the description given by our author appears rather to apply to an oasis in a marsh, or perhaps the Great Sahara, or an island detached from an alluvial delta. It is remarkable that it is placed like a wedge between the Atlas range and the land of the black men. Such-like spots have, we know, at various times formed refuges for races of a different kind to the blacks, where local civilisations were developed, and whence these higher races sallied forth to conquer with fire and sword. We are also told that Tritonia was ultimately submerged, being swallowed up by the sea after a tremendous earthquake, a statement which inclined many to identify the African Amazonia with the lost Atlantis, though that would certainly not tally with the other curious topographical details given by Diodorus.

Our Sicilian historian goes on to say that the Amazons soon conquered the whole of the island, with the exception of Mene, the sacred city of the "fish-eaters." They wore no armour, clothing themselves in the skins of snakes, which approximates these women to witch doctors or priestesses of some form of sun worship, for snakes are connected with magic and the sun. Down to these days snakes are among the most treasured fetishes of the natives of this part of the country, and another sun animal, the crocodile, was associated with the modern royal Amazons of Dahomey. The ancient ones had for arms the bow and arrow and the sword. Thus they are clearly differentiated in religion and war panoply from the Themysciran Amazons. In Africa, as in Asia, the lust of conquest proved irresistible. Queen Merina, assembling an army of 30,000 infantry women and 2000 horse, entered the Land of the Blacks, attacking the Atlantides, capturing their chief towns, and putting every man to the sword. This politic rigour had the desired effect: the whole country submitted to the yoke of the Amazons, who placed the men under vassalage to be ruled over by women governors, and recruited fresh warriors from among the strongest of their own sex. Apparently while Merina was away, Hercules, coming west, had marked the extreme limits of his conquests by erecting his Pillars (the triumphal and thanksgiving[1] columnos usually built as symbols of possession) on the twin rocks of Calpe and Abyla, where the Iberian peninsula most nearly touches the African coast, passed over to the Hesperides, attacked the Amazons, destroying their power in the west, as he had attempted to do in the east. Other writers say that Hercules delivered his crushing blow to the

[1] These were the pillars which the Spanish monarchs were to assume as part of their heraldic insignia, and which their lieutenants still later were to imitate when taking possession of huge tracts of country in the New World in the name of their sovereigns.

I.—COMBAT OF HERCULES AND AMAZONS.
KYLIX. BRITISH MUSEUM.

II.—ACHILLES SLAYING PENTHESILEIA.
AMPHERA (WINE JAR), BRITISH MUSEUM.

Facing page 112.]

strength of the Libyan Amazons either in the Ionian Isles or in Egypt.

Of Merina we are told that she marched across Africa with her great army, and passing through Ethiopia, came into Egypt, there entering into a league with Horus, a sun god and son of the moon gods, Osiris and Isis. Strengthened by such an alliance, she subdued the Arabs, conquered Syria, and receiving the submission of the Cilicians, passed through Phrygia to the Mediterranean. Towns were founded and colonies also planted as the triumphant march progressed. The Mediterranean offered no obstacle to the conquering host: Lesbos and other islands fell to the Amazons. Cast ashore on Samos after a terrific storm, one of those sudden furies to which that sea is so liable, they erected a temple in accordance with a vow taken in the hour of peril. Exhausted by their long warfare, the Amazons succumbed to the fierce attacks of large Greek and Greecised armies led by Mompsus the Thracian and Sypylus the Scythian, and on the death of Merina the African Amazons ceased to exist as a nation. So far Diodorus. Other writers incline to the idea of an eastern invasion of Libya. They say that Egypt was overrun by the Scythian Amazons, as it undoubtedly had been invaded before by various martial Asiatics, and was subsequently to be by the Persians. Of these Amazons some are said to have returned to the Greek isles, some wandered westward across Africa to the Atlantic. A third version is that on the break-up of the Themysciran power certain Amazons made their way from Sarmatia through Gaul and

Iberia to the Atlantic, where they put to sea and captured the Hesperides, returning east across the continent to Egypt.

It is a remarkable fact that the history of Northern Africa presents a record of constant penetration by waves of conquest from the east, now by way of Egypt, and again by white or brown tribes dribbling through the mountainous ranges cutting off the Mediterranean coast fringe, or entering by way of the west. There is a recurring story of white or brown races pushing back the black people and driving a wedge right across the continent, which was rendered possible by the physical character of the country. Lady Lugard describes very fully a trans-continental belt which afforded a vulnerable point in the natural defences of Libya and Ethiopia. First there is the historic Mediterranean coast strip from the Nile to Cape Spartel, then a barrier of grim mountains, but usually with a fairly fertile southern slope, jutting out like feelers into the dreary sandy wastes of the deserts, which stretch right across between latitudes 10° and 15°. Next we have the waterways of the Nile, the Bahr-el-Gazel, the lakes and rivers of Darfour and Wadai, the Shari, Lake Chad, the rivers of Hausaland—the Benne, the Niger, and the Senegal. This chain offers at once a barrier against the southern advance of the sands and provides a fertile subtropical belt, comprising Black Land—the Soudan, Ethiopia, Nigreta, Tekrour, Genowah, in some parts peopled with races of very mixed blood. North of the waterways is the sand ocean, which, in spite of its changing surface, retains a deadly monotony; south of it are in many places dense and gloomy forests, regions inhabited by giants, pigmies, cannibals, and beasts of strange forms. Against all these the white and brown invaders had to battle, a struggle which has left a deep impression on tradition and literature, and not least on the people. That ancient historians knew something of these regions is evident from their descriptions of Ethiopia and Libya, with their natural boundaries of seas, sandy plains, and the, strictly speaking, non-existent but fairly well represented river Oceanus. And then there is the Semitic and Asiatic invasion, both direct by way of the Nile and south-westward through the Atlas ranges. It is the echoes of such emigrations that we have in Diodorus's account of the eastward march of the Libyan Amazons.

Herodotus, writing of the Libyan tribes, refers to the Zavecians, "whose wives drive their chariots to battle," a custom which must have been introduced into Northern Africa from Asia through Syria.

Philology is also not without its interest in this matter. Mr. J. C. Prichard, quoting M. Venture, says that the Berbers (of unquestioned Asiatic origin) inhabiting the Northern Atlas call their language Amazigh, which has been translated as "the noble language." There have been some authors who trace the word Amazon from this term. However that may be, it is certain that these tribes of Northern Africa have bred many valiant fighting women. When in the seventy-seventh year of Hegira the Moslems under Hossan Ibn Annoman captured Carthage and sent the Imperial troops packing in hot haste to Constantinople, they suddenly found themselves confronted by a more formidable enemy. This was a native queen, Dhabba, whom the Arabs called Cahina or "The Sorceress." She was regarded as a saint and magician by her people, and had contrived to enlist under her banner the wild Moors from Mauritania and the Berbers from the verge of the desert and the fastnesses of the Atlas range, also receiving active support from the civilised dwellers of the flat coast strip and its many wealthy walled towns. Dhabba proved victorious, and caused Hossan and his Moslem host to retire to Egypt. But after all she was a barbarian, and her patriotism took a barbaric turn. Pointing out that the followers of Mahomet were attracted to their country by the rich towns, the beautiful gardens with their groves of fruit trees, she advised her troops to dismantle the town walls, to pull down majestic buildings, uproot the prolific gardens, and hew down the fruit orchards. The nomads from the desert, the semi-troglodytes from mountain ranges were nothing loth, and the whole country was quickly converted into a howling wilderness. It was a costly mistake, for thereby the numerous and powerful seaboard population was rendered hostile, and when Hossan returned with greater forces, he found the queen's legions thinned and the coastal people anxious to welcome him. Dhabba, in spite of her bravery, was defeated, and, refusing to submit, was beheaded.

Returning to the Upper Nile, we find Sir George Rawlinson stating that in his days the king of the Behrs on the White Nile had a guard of women, who protected him so effectually that no man could approach his person except his ministers, who came to strangle him when he was nearing his end—a gentle attention designed to prevent his departing this world as a mere common disease-ridden mortal. But we may well ask whether this guard and the gruesome custom had not a profounder meaning. We are tempted to see in the petty sovereign a representative of a once god-king, whose duty and high privilege it was to offer his life as a sacrifice for the good of his people, he himself merely hastening his journey, and then these guards would be recognised as successors to priestesses. Certainly the conjunction of attendants and custom is suggestive of Asiatic practices. As late as 1840, M. d'Arnaud found the king of the Behrs surrounded by a body of spearswomen.

It was somewhere in this neighbourhood that Father Alvares gathered information concerning an Amazonian nation differing widely from the classical type. The father accompanied the Portuguese Ambassador to the Court of Prester John, Emperor of Abyssinia in 1520–1527, and in his quaintly straightforward narrative of the mission he gives an account of the tributary kingdoms of Damute and Gorage, which lay to the south-west of Prester John's territories. After this he adds: "They say that at the extremity of these kingdoms of Damute and Gorage, towards the south, is what may be called the kingdom of the Amazons; but not so,—as it seems to me, or as it has been told to me, or as the book of Infante Don Pedro related or relates to us,—because these Amazons (if these are so) all have husbands generally throughout the year, and always at all times with them, and pass their life with their husbands. They have not a king, but have a queen. She is not married, nor has she any special husband, but withal does not omit having sons and daughters, and her daughter is the heir to the kingdom. They say that they are women of a very warlike disposition, and they fight riding on certain animals, light, strong, and agile, like cows, and are great archers; and when they are little they dry up the left breast, in order not to impede drawing the arrow. They also say that there is very much gold in this kingdom of the Amazons, and that it comes from this country to the kingdom of Damute, and so it goes to many parts. They say that the husbands of these women are not warriors, and that their wives dispense them from it. They say that a great river has its source in the kingdom of Damute, and opposite to the Nile, because each one goes in its own direction, the Nile to Egypt: of this other no one in the country knows where it goes to, only it is presumed that it goes to Manicuigo." Here we have sufficient details of what appears to have been a matriarchal state, peculiar in this, that the women were trained as warriors, but not Amazonian as described at Themyscira, though the drying-up of one breast is certainly suggestive of the Asiatic practice. But it is the account of a complete community, like that of the Sauromatœ Gynœcocratumeni, merely with the special social functions reversed; thus it does not fall into the same class as the Grecian myth of the unnatural state, which no doubt explains the cautious hesitation of the reverend chronicler.

Father Jaos dos Santos, who had preceded Alvares, visiting Abyssinia as a missionary in 1506, says: "In the neighbourhood of Damute is a province in which the women are so much addicted to war and hunting that they constantly go armed. When contention fails in their neighbourhood they purposely excite quarrels among themselves, that they may exercise their skill and courage, and neither the one be injured nor the other relaxed by idleness. They are much more daring than the men of the country, and that they may have no impediment to the proper exercise of their right arm, they are accustomed, while their daughters are young, to sear the breast of that side with a hot iron, and thus wither it to prevent growth. Most of the women are more occupied with warfare than the management of their domestic affairs, whence they rarely marry, and live as formerly did the Amazons of Themyscira. Where by chance any enter the marriage state and have children, they take charge of them no longer than till they are weaned, after which they send them to their fathers to be brought up. But the chief of them imitate the example of their queen, who lives in a state of perpetual virginity, and is regarded as a deity by her subjects—nay, even all the sovereigns whose territories are adjacent to hers pride themselves on living with her on friendly terms, and defend her against any attack. Indeed, the power of this monarch is such as to make her another Queen of Sheba, whose authority over her subjects, as is related by the Patriarch Bermudes in his book on Prester John, was without limit. The same patriarch relates that off the coast of China islands are found peopled with Amazons who suffer no man among them except at certain seasons, for the preservation of the race."

This mention of Chinese islands reminds us that Socotra was also said to be an Amazon island, while others declare that the dual Male and Female islands, wherein, as Marco Polo describes, the sexes lived apart with only periodical visits, lay off Socotra. Thomas Wright, in a note on Marco Polo's travels, refers to two different maps whereon these islets were marked respectively as "Les Deux Frères" and "Les Deux Sœurs." This, however, might well have been in allusion to their nearness and similarity of outline. The naming of localities by discoverers is generally determined on a very lax system, and therefore proves a dangerous guide for shaping any theories. For instance, we know that William Baffin during his explorations in the Arctic regions in 1616 named an islet Women Island because they first met women there after several months of isolation, yet he says that men were with them. So it comes about that much of the nomenclature of new-found lands is misleading, because it is determined by accidents often of a trivial nature.

As for Father dos Santos, his reference to the quarrelsomeness of the women may be put down to professional zeal; but his remarks about the queen are most instructive. Her condition of life was certainly not that attributed to the Asiatic Amazon sovereigns, and seems to have reference to a sacred priest-queen, whose life was a consecration, if not a sacrifice. The alleged attitude of the neighbouring chiefs, who desired to be on friendly terms with her and deemed it an honour to defend her dominions, rather confirms this view. Father Alvares paints a less pleasing picture, but one closer to classic examples. On the other hand, the lapse of some twenty years between the two accounts may well have brought about changes, notably in the dignity of the ruler. Another Portuguese priest, the celebrated Don Jao Bermudes, patriarch and presbyter, who was sent on a religious mission to Prester John's country, rather tends to confirm the version of dos Santos, for he too, in describing the province of women near Damute, says that "the queen of these women knoweth no man, and for that act is worshipped among them as a goddess." This worthy patriarch categorically avers that the nation owed its origin to the Queen of Sheba. But he was fond of dogmatic statements, somewhat greedy of marvels, so much so that his lively accounts of various animals—among others, vultures which could lift and fly away with buffaloes—drew down a scathing rebuke from the industrious Samuel Purchas, the famous collector and translator of voyages; then this worthy editor, having cried out against the fables and the fabulists, adds, with the true note of the philosophy of doubt: "And yet may Africa have a prerogative in rarities, and some seeming incredulities be true," a fact which we of this generation have proved in more than one connection, though not in all, that has been said of the mysteries of the Dark Continent.

It is, at first sight, somewhat of a far cry from these regions of the White Nile to the coast of

Guinea, yet, as we have seen, it is on that line of waterways which form a chain across the continent. At this other extremity we find considerable traces of Amazonian organisation dating back at least several centuries. While Father Alvares describes a woman-dominated state, with women warriors, in the East, M. d'Arnaud and others give us glimpses of female guards on the Upper Nile, and earlier travellers tell us of Amazonian forces in the Congo and Guinea, the latter the very region of which Diodorus Siculus appears to write, the first clear account being of the Monomotapa women soldiers given by Pigafetta, and of the Dahomeyan Amazons penned by explorers between 1703–1730. The latest to deal at any length with the subject of the Dahomeyans is M. Foa, who gave in 1890 many details of the country and the mettle of the women soldiers as proved by their encounters with the French under General Dodd. He says that the force only dates back to the early days of the last century, when Gezo created the female army as a means to guard against a similar accident to that which befell his brother Admozan, who was dethroned by a popular rising. That is, of course, a mistake, as the records of European travellers go back to the early part of the eighteenth century, when the force was apparently old and well-established. Gezo, as a matter of fact, was merely the reorganiser, and in passing we may take note of the curious name of the dethroned brother, which appears to link us up with the Berbers of the north and the Kaffirs of the east, south of the equator. According to M. Foa, Gezo recruited his

Amazons from among slave women taken in war. For this purpose young and strong women were chosen, who were confined to the precincts of the royal palace and subjected to a most severe training. The Amazons formed an exact counterpart of the regular army, the officers being women who held equal rank with the men leaders. Many of these female warriors were allowed to marry. They formed part of the standing army, and were at one time 10,000 strong, headed by a Royal Guard of Elephant Hunters, who wore trousers reaching to the knee, short skirts, a linen strip over the upper part of the body, and antlers fixed to their caps. The ordinary women soldiers wore the same uniform but with a small cap adorned with a tortoise badge cut out of blue cloth. They had their heads shaved, and necklaces of beads and amulets hung from their necks. Their arms consisted of short Dahomeyan swords,—a kind of scimitar,—battle-axes, bows and arrows, and flint-lock guns. But the French authority describes the women as anything but good shots with gun or bow, though in hand-to-hand fights they proved exceedingly fierce, and generally victorious over native tribes. These Amazons were allowed all kinds of privileges, having precedence of every one except the chiefs, and when they went forth a small girl preceded them, ringing a bell, so that all men and ordinary women should stand aside and afford a free passage to the truculent warriors, who, we are told, were very masculine and extremely ugly.

M. Foa seems to have been rather hasty in his generalisations, though doubtless accurate enough in describing what he actually saw. But an English traveller had written an account in 1708 of what came under his own observation, and he says that the then King of Dahomey had a great number of women armed like soldiers, "having their proper officers, and furnished like regular troops with drums, colours, and umbrellas." It is also recorded that in 1728 and 1729 the king conquered the combined forces of Wydah and Popos with his Amazonian troops, an account of this expedition being given by Archibald Dalzel, sometime Governor of the Gold Coast, in a book published in 1793, but written many years before. Commander Frederick Forbes, who was in the country for a considerable time, also has much to say about these forces, which he understood were of very ancient origin. He describes them as wonderfully strong and agile, and divided into numerous corps.

Another French observer, the Abbé Laffitte, who was in Dahomey about 1870, had a poor opinion of the morals of these women, but he attests to their bravery and their staunchness to the king. When Gezo attacked Abeokuta and was repulsed with great slaughter, he was personally in great danger, for the men fled, leaving their king at the mercy of the enemy. Had it not been for the Amazons, who stood firm to guard his retreat, Gezo would inevitably have been captured. On this occasion the greater number of the women were left dead on the field. Gezo's successor also attempted to capture Abeokuta, and it was again the Amazons who prevented the retreat being converted into a disastrous defeat, they engaging the enemy while the king sought safety in flight. Abeokuta, by the way, had always been a thorn in the side of their Dahomey majesties. It was a community formed by natives who had been persecuted by the *razias* of the Amazons, and taking refuge under a rocky hillside, had built themselves a fortified town, which proved impregnable. It is in Yoruba, and its name literally means "under the rocks." In Burton's time, however, the king deemed himself of such importance that he remained in semi-seclusion, and nobody but members of his own family and servants were permitted to see him eat, drink, or take snuff. In Laffitte's time the Amazons were allowed to marry, but only if they were too old or too feeble for warfare. It would seem to have been an economical method of pensioning off used-up warriors. They were, the abbé affirms, hard workers, for the king gave them no rations or pay; so, at all events before marriage, they had to earn their living by labour.

Sir Richard Burton, after his second visit to Dahomey, wrote at once amusingly and instructively on the whole subject. His evidence certainly points conclusively to a long past, though he is by no means inclined to be romantic over either the traditions or persons. He asserts that Gezo had reorganised the force, and for this purpose chose recruits from the most comely and fit daughters of his chiefs. Moreover, they seemed to have, at least nominally, formed part of his harem; so the marriage arrangements, if the French travellers were not mistaken in their facts, must have crept in at a later date, probably to relieve the royal treasury. But there certainly appears to have been considerable variation in the matter of recruiting and organisation.

In Burton's days the Amazon army was composed of the Fanti company of the king's bodyguard, their head-dress consisting of a narrow white cotton fillet with a crocodile cut out of blue cloth sewn on to the band, the hair being cut short, though the head was not shaven. Then there were the right and left wings, including five arms: (1) blunderbuss women, (2) elephant hunters, (3) razor women (who were armed with a razor-like blade, 18 inches long, kept open by means of strong springs, and mounted on a pole 2 feet long), (4) archeresses (carrying the native bow and poisoned arrows), (5) infantry (armed with tower muskets). The elephant hunters appeared to be a *corps de parade*, while the archeresses had evidently degenerated from a former high estate to a mere body of skirmishers and camp-followers. They had knives lashed to their wrists, wore extremely scanty clothing, and had prominent tattoo marks extending down to the knee. The whole force amounted to about 350 royal bodyguard and 2500 women of the line. The gala uniforms were not without a certain gallant and picturesque effect. A narrow fillet of blue or white bound the hair, the bosom was concealed by a sleeveless waistcoat of various colours, buttoning in front and leaving the arms free. Loin-wrappers of blue, pink, or yellow extended to the ankles, and were fastened round the waist by white sashes falling in long floating ends on one side. Bandoliers, bullet-bags, and short knives completed the outfit. The workaday uniforms were rather more summary, consisting of browny grey tunics, armless, but covering the bosom and extending to the knees; short trousers; and sashes. The bow and arrow women, as we have already said, had a far more primitive costume, probably with the idea of being more adapted for rough camp and bush work. The officers of all arms were distinguished in various ways. Burton says that the female commander-in-chief, who was one of the king's councillors, was a dame of vast proportions. The captain of the royal bodyguard wore a "bonnet like that of a French cordon-bleu, but pink and white below, with two crocodiles of blue cloth on the top, the whole confined by silver horns and lanyards." Another commandress had a silver hammerhead projecting above her eyes, which gave her the semblance of a unicorn. Considering her proportions, this irresistibly reminds us that Pausanias says that the Ethiopian bulls have horns on their noses, evidently referring to the rhinoceros, that unwieldy prototype of the fabled elegant and agile unicorn. All chief women had umbrellas of state, usually emblazoned with their badges of office, also special standards and girl orderlies to carry their guns. The Amazonian bands comprised players on cymbals, drums, and rattles. Much of the manœuvring consisted of elaborate dancing, sometimes in companies or in small groups, with frequent *pas de seul.*

The Abbé Pierre Bouché, who had seen much missionary service in Guinea and the hinterland, gives quite a different version as regards the recruiting of the Amazons. He says they were chosen from among (1) criminals, (2) the unfaithful in matters matrimonial, (3) nagging wives. Even in Burton's time nagging wives and other social nuisances were "dashed" to the king for service in his army, and there can be little doubt that practice in this direction differed from time to time. But Burton is positive that the harem restrictions were rigorous enough. Bouché, however, like Laffitte, had no high opinion of them morally, though of their courage and capacity for physical endurance he was in no doubt whatever, and he founded his opinion *pour et contre* both from what he saw and what he had heard from trustworthy witnesses. The abbé quotes a graphic description of a full-dress war-rehearsal at which M. Borghero was present somewhere about 1880. On an open square was erected a broad hedge of prickly cactus; beyond this was a clear space, then a timber house with steeply slanting roof, and beyond that a collection of huts. Three thousand Amazons were mustered, and they had to take the "village" (represented by the cluster of huts) by assault and by a frontal attack. This little game was complicated by the usual conventions which complicate all war games the world over: it was understood that the warriors were to be thrice repulsed (by non-existent defenders) in their assaults on the fort (or aforementioned timber house). M. Borghero was stupefied by the dash and pluck of the women, who swarmed over the prickly barrier with bare feet, scaled the house, twice retired hurriedly, but at the third assault, clambering up the house, slithered down on the opposite side, and then scampered off to surround and enter the huts.

Undoubtedly the Amazons were held in great honour, and accordingly held themselves high in their own esteem; but while they took precedence, they declared, "We are no longer females, we are males," and the most deadly insult to a soldier was to call him a woman. These contradictions clearly point to

FIGURES FROM CRATES. DEATH OF PRIAM AT THE TAKING OF TROY.

Facing page 129.]

considerable changes in an old organisation whose origin was practically forgotten. It certainly can have had nothing to do with any matriarchal form of society, for it tends to show a respect not for women, but for a privileged caste. The official title of the Amazons was Akho-si, that is, "King's Wives," and their popular name Mi-no, or "our mothers." These terms are, of course, conventional. In the *Arabian Nights* a great Far Eastern king, whose daughter ruled the island of El-Wak-Wak, called his 25,000 mounted lancer women "his daughters," and in Moslem lands it is usual to address an unknown woman, no matter what her age, as "O my mother," merely as a token of honourable intentions. It is possible that the harem arrangement was merely a survival from an old form of royal guard similar to that of the kings of Behr, itself a probable modification of the priestess attendants on a god-king. This would account for the anomaly in the sentiment shown as regards the position of women. On the other hand, Winwood Reade tells us that a princess of the Congo could marry whom she pleased, but the husband had to assume a female name and feminine attire, cover his face, and when he went out he was preceded by a slave beating a drum to clear the way.

It will have been noticed that M. Foa states that the Amazons wore a blue tortoise badge on their head-dresses. Whether this was a degenerate form of the blue crocodile seen by Forbes and Burton, or a special fetish of the then reigning king, it is hard to say. The tortoise is one of the amphibians specially honoured by most primitive races, for in their cosmogonies he replaces Atlas, bearing the weight of created world on his carapace. One thing is certain, the crocodile, another amphibian, is most significant locally, for Tokpodun was the crocodile god worshipped in many districts hereabouts, and crocodiles played their part in some of the sacrificial ceremonies, or annual "customs," as he did in Egypt. Lisa, the sun god, had a chameleon as messenger, a kind of Mercury. Snake worship is general throughout Dahomey and well beyond its confines. The python is regarded as the representative of the god who brings good and evil, and is sacred. Danhgbwe, "the snake mother," a small brown and white striped boa, is worshipped at Wydah; the great fetish of the hunters and foresters is Gbwe-ji, a small snake marked like a boa, while Aydo-whe-ho is the heavenly rainbow of the local pantheon, and is represented by a coiled horned snake. Vodun is the snake fetish of the slave coast, and, as we know by Bosman and the dark doings in Hayti, "voodoo" worship involves dancing orgies, in which women take part, and human sacrifice. All this is not without interest, for it brings us back to the snake-clothed, scimitar-bearing Amazons of Diodorus, connecting the warrior women with snake worship, the religious organisation, and, therefore, the kingship.

It is difficult to form an accurate idea as to their numbers, for there have always been considerable divergence in estimates. At times they appear to have been so numerous as to depopulate the country, partly as a result of their organisation, and partly owing to the frequent forays which the existence of a considerable body of warriors rendered necessary. Early travellers, however, were apt to carry away an erroneous impression of the military strength of the kings of Dahomey, because these astute persons were fond of adopting an ingenious *ruse de guerre*, marching their Amazons across the open exercise ground from the mud gates of the women's compounds to a thicket, the women then doubling back behind the trees to their old quarters, and emerging once more, thus forming units of an endless army. It is an illustration of one of those spontaneously evolved stratagems that may occur to people of very different ways of thinking. We have seen it in our own land, when the red-shawled women of Fishguard passed to and fro on the hillsides in order to deceive the French. This has been dubbed noble with us, though the Dahomeyans have been derided for their methods, which have been likened to the shifts of economically minded theatrical managers; some have even grown indignant at the deception. But indeed we are far too ready to hold the use of a simulacrum in contempt as a mere degrading subterfuge, a symbol, as it were, of hypocrisy. Often, no doubt, 'tis little but the homage paid by vice to virtue. Occasionally, on the contrary, and this more frequently than the unphilosophical allow for, it is the stepping-stone to higher things. Discontented with affairs as they exist, the husk is retained, the essential being neglected while groping about for the better. And these, dry husks though they are, may be infinitely preferable to the real thing, "the essential."

Thus, when men grew doubtful as to the ethics of slaughtering slaves to the end that they might be buried with their dead lord, so that a worldly servitude should be continued by ghostly drudgery in the Land of Shades; or of the justice of decapitating a prisoner of war in order that he should become a sleepless sentry, his grinning head being stuck on a long pole to keep never-ceasing guard over the captain's hut or grave; and in their doubt substituted clay dolls, painted effigies, or dropped into the yawning grave whole troops of men, women, and little children scored on bark, stone slabs, or other convenient materials, and placed a graven image as a guard over the tomb instead of a genuine skull or stuffed skin—the simulacra proved an advance on the real things. No doubt they were mere empty forms, and suspiciously profitable to the surviving relatives, but they certainly were a gain to potential victims and to humanity. So when His Majesty of Dahomey had to eke out his thinned Amazonian bands by a trick, the subterfuge showed that growing humane feeling or exhaustion (which may powerfully help towards virtuous deeds) had depleted his hungry army, to the relief of his own country and his neighbours', and here too the make-believe was an improvement on the reality. Humanity is a frail thing, and is rarely strong enough to be off with the old love before it is on with the new.

As we have said, Dahomey is not the only country on the west coast where Amazons have been employed within modern times. The King of Yoruba had a woman bodyguard, so numerous, indeed, that the dusky monarch boasted that if they clasped hands they would reach across the kingdom; while in Bosman's day the petty King of Wydah had from 4000 to 5000 "wives," who executed the royal sentences. Moreover, we have a link connecting the West with

Central and Eastern Africa. This is afforded by a spirited account by Pigafetta of the many adventures of Eduardo Lopez, who was in the kingdom of the Congo about 1580. In describing the empire of Monomotapa, he says that among the soldiers were legions of fighting women. They were highly esteemed, used the bow and arrow with considerable dexterity, and, in order to facilitate their doing so, burnt away the right breast. We are told that "they are very quick and swift, lively and courageous, and very cunning in shooting, but especially and above all venturous and constant in fight." They used cunning, often appearing to run before the enemy, and then turning to resist their advance. When hard pressed they dispersed in all directions, then, circling about, encompassed the foe on all sides. According to these Portuguese observers, the women enjoyed the king's favour, and had certain countries, or districts, assigned to them, where they brought up the female children, but sent away the boys at an early age. Lopez reported that in the north-east of the Congo Empire, "at the beginning of the Nilus," there dwelt the monstrous tribe of Giachas, or Agagi, giants who "feed upon man's flesh," who scarred their lips and cheeks with certain lines made with red-hot irons,[1] and who were at con-

[1] Tattoo marks are used primarily ast ribal and professional badges, originally being connected with totemism, the adornment for the sake of personal attraction or repulsion (in love matters or warfare) being a natural development of the system. Ancient legends say that the Annamites, being in sore danger from monsters of the air and sea, tattooed themselves so as to resemble dragons and fishes, becoming brothers thereof. Hence, probably, the wonderful dragons and fishes spread all over China and Japan. Man held himself as a descendant of fierce animals, and adorned his body with cicatrices, dyes, or skins

tinual war with the Congolese Amazons, evidently engaged in the attempt to penetrate to a more fertile country, being pressed by the barbarian invasion of their own country, as explained in the early part of this chapter.

We have a kind of echo of this from Father Giovanni Antonio Cavazzi, in his absorbing history of Ethiopia, wherein, referring to the Congo, he says that in 1640 Llinga, a daughter of the late king, succeeded him, but, refusing to submit to Portuguese supervision, was driven from her country. However, she seems to have been well endowed mentally and to have exhibited considerable qualities as a ruler, as well as those of a warrior, for she kept a large following, carried on armed resistance for a long time,

accordingly. Hence the use of the pelts of lions, leopards, and buffaloes, the cloaks of birds' feathers, the snake coverings of the Libyan Amazons, and the peculiar clothing of the present-day "Fish-Skinned" Tatars of the Amur. It is curious to find that in Bruce's time certain tribes of the Sudan tattooed their stomachs, sides, and back with fish-scales. The god-king and priest-king, who sat on the thrones provided with animals' feet and birds' claws, and had footstools of their ancestral beasts, when they died were often depicted so as to show this peculiar union, and they appear with the body of a lion or the head of an eagle. The priestly class and devotees tattooed themselves with the symbols of their deities. That the practice was regarded as idolatrous is shown in Leviticus, where we read (xix. 28): "Ye shall not make any cuttings in your flesh for the dead nor print any marks upon you." Pliny, who speaks of the Moseyni, who dwelt near Themyscira, as a tribe "who make marks upon their bodies," said that the Daci also made scars on their arms to denote their origin, and that these marks were reproduced on new-born babes unto the fourth generation, though Aristotle holds that these birth-marks disappeared after the third. As regards the sacerdotal use of cicatricial tattooings, M. Foa says that the priests and priestesses of Dahomey, especially those of the Serpent and Thunder, were horribly tattooed. One peculiar form was like a web. A number of filaments of skin were arranged in concentric circles and united by cross filaments to a central knob of skin, the whole design being detached from the body except returned to the Congo, and forced peace on the wearied Portuguese. She clad herself in skins, carried axe, bows and arrows, and a sword. Even after her return she made strife a profession, probably in order to maintain her supremacy among a turbulent people; and one of her amiable customs was to offer a man as a sacrifice before going to war, striking off his head with her sword and publicly drinking his blood. She apparently had female assistants in her tyranny. Father Cavazzi goes on to tell us of another Amazonian virago in this region who cherished designs of forming a state of warrior women. Early in the sixteenth century the Congo was invaded from the north-east by the stalwart fighting Jagas. So it will be seen that the cannibal giants of Lopez'

at its outer circle. This is undoubtedly of a symbolical nature, referring to mysteries and magic. Much of the tattooing is conventionalised to the extreme limit, differing from the practice of the Pacific islanders or the paintings of American Indians. For instance, the turkey totem of the Lenapé is represented by the imprint of the claw; on the west coast of Africa the horns of the antelope by two curved lines (also seen in India); while the tortoise is shown as a square, with projecting outline for the four paws, and a straight bar across for the head and tail. Much of the tattooing in Africa on the lips and cheeks, as was the case with the Nile Jagas, or on the forehead and breast, on the trunk as with the Sudan fish tribe, or on the legs as with the Dahomeyan elephant huntresses, consists of mere dots and lines, occasionally with curves (or snakey lines). Now, it is to be noted that the divination board, somewhat like an exaggerated backgammon board, with its men of sacred palm kernels, is widely used. The combination of numbers seems to be closely connected with notions of religious organisations—the different spheres of action, number of gods, hierarchy of priests, and so on. This idea of numbers we find among the Assyrians, where Anu, the Creator, was represented by the number 60; Sin, the sun god, by 30; Ishtar, the moon goddess, by 15. It has to do with the mystery of numbers, whence the sacredness of the numbers three and seven, and the mathematical jugglings of the magicians, white or black, and was, no doubt, derived from astrology and the practical application thereof.

days still harried the kingdom. The Jagas committed great ravages under their chief, Zimbo. He, however, was ultimately defeated and driven south. Journeying towards the Cape, he suddenly turned north, and creeping up the coast, settled on the banks of the Cunene River, where he formed a kingdom. On his death Zimbo was succeeded by one of his captains, who in turn was succeeded by his wife, Mussasa. Their daughter, Tembandumba, had been named after the celebrated consort of Zimbo, and was brought up to warlike pursuits.

It is a matter for curious conjecture whether this warlike training of the Jagas women was due to their experiences on the Upper Nile or to their contact with the old Amazonian troops of Monomotapa. In any case, while still quite young, Tembandumba seems to have nourished ambitious projects, and, the better to attain them, associated with herself a number of young girls, training them by fighting and hunting. She declined to be ruled by convention, and only entered into temporary matrimonial alliances, though scrupulously killing her lovers after very brief dalliance. Thus she, at all events, was always unmistakably off with the old love before she was on with the new. Her next act of self-assertion was to rebel against Mussasa and proclaim herself queen. She then organised the nation on a war footing. She commanded that all male infants, all twins, all females whose upper teeth appeared before their lower ones, and all those born within villages, should be killed by their mothers, the bodies pounded in mortars and, mixed with herbs, converted into magic ointment. Temporary husbands were to be captured by force of arms. The better to enforce male infant sacrifice, the queen assembled the tribe, and tearing her baby boy from her breast, flung him into a mortar and pounded him to death, adding herbs and roots, and forming an ointment which she rubbed all over her body, declaring herself thus rendered invulnerable. Other mothers, seized with imitative frenzy, did as the queen did, and then followed her to war. Before long, however, there arose a certain amount of passive resistance; male infants were kept in secret, and Tembandumba had to appoint officers to slay new-born babes.

Finally, she had to abandon her idea of the woman state, and she accepted male infants captured in war for ointment-manufacturing purposes. The tribe was cannibalistic and offered human sacrifices; women, however, were only killed on the death of great chiefs, first as a matter of enforced routine, and later as voluntary candidates for post-mortem honours. Tembandumba kept her people in continual strife, ruling mainly through women. Then she fell under the spell of one of her husbands, and, tolerating him too long, was poisoned when she began to manifest tokens of conjugal unrest. She was a repulsive-looking creature, and her magic ointment had not been used as an eye salve, for she lost one of them in battle. Thus ended this curious experiment, which may be paralleled with the traditions of Valasca's rule in Bohemia. But Cavazzi's story is mainly that of abnormality. Unless we conjecture that the Jagas brought their women-warrior and women-ruling proclivities from the Nile basin, it is less significant than that of Edward Lopez, whose tale of a royal female guard employed on desperate undertakings links up the Congo with Guinea and the White Nile, and so, in a sense, completes this African circle, stretching from Abyssinia to Dahomey, with a great loop south of the equator, taking in this Cunene colony as its extreme limit.

CHAPTER VIII

Amazons of America

When Christopher Columbus was returning from his first voyage of discovery, he was told by the Indians of Hispaniola of another island, called Mantinino, which was inhabited solely by women. They employed themselves in labour not suited to their sex, using the bow and arrow, hunting, and going to war. Once a year they received Caribs from other islands among them, the men only staying a short time, and on their next annual visit taking away with them the male infants that had been born, the girls remaining with their mothers. These women, besides using bows and arrows, had defensive armour of brass plates. This intelligence added to the admiral's conviction that he was on the coast of the Indies, for the ancients had spoken of islands where the Themysciran Amazons had taken refuge, and one of his own countrymen, a great traveller by land, the Venetian, Marco Polo, as we know, had given an account of what was considered by many as their last abode. But although Columbus constantly heard rumours of the mysterious island, which often seemed to be in the immediate neighbourhood, yet ever receded, he was not destined to see it or any of its inhabitants. No one, indeed, succeeded in identifying the particular island of which the natives of the Caribbean Sea seemed to give such explicit details. Other Spanish adventurers, however, had different tales to tell.

In 1540, some forty years after Allonzo Pinzon had discovered the great Marañon, Francesco de Orellana, making his way from far-off Peru to the Atlantic through the Brazils, explored the magnificent river, he and his companions meeting with many difficulties. They were told of a race of pigmies, of men whose heads grew out of their backs, of others whose feet were turned the wrong way round, so that if any one attempted to follow in their tracks, the pursuers were misled, actually receding from those they desired to catch up. There were also men with tails, and stories of the Ozacoulets, a tribe of warriors with white skins, blue eyes, and long light-coloured beards; but most persistent of all were the rumours of warrior women who lived apart from men. The grandeur and novelty of the scenes they were passing through, the weirdness of the stories they heard, all prepared the Spanish adventurers to accept the marvellous, so that when they had accomplished rather more than half of their journey, and were approaching the Trombetus River in the neighbourhood of the great, densely wooded island of Tumpinambaranas, formed by the junction of the Madera with the Marañon, they found themselves opposed by warlike natives gathered on the banks, and among them noticed women seemingly acting as leaders of the men, they readily fell into the notion that here they had stumbled upon the renowned Amazons. In this belief they were confirmed by the natives whom they cross-examined, and de Orellana, duly impressed with this wonderful discovery, and some say actuated by a desire to magnify his own exploits, renamed the Marañon River the Amazon, a name subsequently given to a whole vast province.

Garcilaso Inca de la Vega, in his account of the expedition of Gonzalo Pizarro and his lieutenants, quotes Father Carbajal, who was in the train of de Orellana. The good father says that the Indians attacked the small but well-armed party of Spaniards so fiercely because they were tributaries to the Amazons, which betrays a certain confusion of ideas with Asiatic traditions. However, he and others of his Spanish companions saw some ten or twelve Amazons who were fighting in the front ranks of the Indians, acting as though they were in command, and with such vigour that the Indians did not dare to turn their backs, and those who fled before the enemy were killed with sticks by their own party. These women appeared to be very tall, robust, fair of complexion, with long hair twisted over their heads, skins of wild beasts wound round their loins, and carried bows and arrows in their hands, with which they killed many of the explorer's party.

These rumours of the Amazonian nation were plentiful, but no one ever came across the country, at least no one of sufficient standing to give accurate geographical indications. The country was supposed to be buried in the gloomy forests, though it was said to possess rich cities. Some time after the adventure of de Orellana and Carbajal, another missionary, Father Cristobal de Acuña, who had long dwelt in the Brazils, gave, in his *New Discovery of the Great River of the Amazons*, considerably more details. "These man-like women," he writes, "have their abodes in the extensive forests and lofty hills, among which that which rises above the rest, and is therefore beaten by the winds for its pride with most violence, so that it is bare and clear of vegetation, is called Yacamiaba. The Amazons are women of great valour, and they have always preserved themselves without the ordinary intercourse with men; and even when these, by agreement, come every year to their land, they receive them with arms in their hands, such as bows and arrows, which they brandish about for a time, until they are satisfied that the Indians come with peaceful intentions. They then drop their arms and go down to the canoes of their guests, where each one chooses a hammock, the nearest at hand, which they take to their own houses, and, hanging them in a place where their owners could recognise them, they receive the Indians as guests for a few days. After this the Indians return to their own country, repeating their visits every year at the same season. The daughters who are born from this intercourse are preserved and brought up by the Amazons themselves, as they are destined to inherit their valour and the customs of the nation; but it is not so certain what they do with the sons. An Indian who had gone with his father to this country when very young stated that the boys were given to their fathers when they returned the following year. But others—and they appear most probable, as it is most general—say that when the Amazons find that a baby is a male, they kill it. Time will discover the truth; and if these are the Amazons made famous by historians, there are treasures shut up in their territory which would enrich the whole world." This is much the same story that was gathered by Columbus, though the admiral's will-o'-the-wisp tribe are supposed to be on an island of the Caribbean Sea, while those brought before de Orellana were on the mainland, some said hidden in the forests, others safe on an island formed by the sweep of two rivers, an island like Tumpinambaranas, which is 210 miles long and contains 950 square miles, or, again, on an island in one of the great lakes.

Alas for the good father! time exploded the legend, at least as he understood the matter. Neither Amazon nation nor their fabulous treasures have ever been found. Yet it was not from any want of willingness or energy on the part of the Spaniards. Animated by stories such as those recorded by Acosta and Herrera and sworn to by wandering whites and natives before the Royal Audienza at Quito, there was real enthusiasm and emulation displayed in furthering exploration for this constantly receding country "where women alone are." Nuño de Gusman, writing in July 1530 from Omittan to the Emperor Charles V. (Charles I. of Spain), says, with cheerful anticipation of what was in store for a lucky and enterprising Don, "I shall go to find the Amazons, which some say dwell in the sea, some in an arm of the sea, and that they are rich and accounted of the people for goodness, and whiter than other women. They use bows and arrows and targets; have many great treasures." We find, among others, Hernando de Ribera conducting a search party. He came across many natives who reported to him that beyond the Mansion of the Sun—that is to say, westward of a great lake wherein the sun sank daily to rest—there would be found that much-sought-after country "where women alone dwelt." This might allude even to Peru, where, among the Cordilleras of the Andes, temples of the sun had been built on high mountains, such as Intihuatana, "the Seat of the Sun," a fortress temple on a high hill near Cuzco, in the vicinity of Lake Titikaka, some 1300 feet above sea-level. There was, however, no record of women warriors on that side of the Andes, at all events in the days of the Incas. To return to Brazil, Ribera was told that the women possessed both white and yellow metal (silver and gold) in such abundance that they made their seats and household utensils out of them. Close neighbours of theirs, so it was said, were the pigmies, who formed a nation by themselves. About forty-seven years later Anthony Knivet, who went with Thomas Candish on his second voyage to the South Seas, was captured by the Portuguese, escaped, and wandered through Brazil. He heard of the Amazons, and, indeed, claimed that his Indian companions said that they traversed the mysterious country; but when Knivet urged an attack on the women, the natives "durst not, for they said, We know that the country is very populous, and we shall all be killed."

On the other hand, we hear rumours of the Amazons in quite another direction. Sir Walter Raleigh, in his *Discovery of Guiana*, says that he spoke to a cacique who had been to the Amazon River and beyond. This chief reported that "the

I.—FIGURES FROM CRATES FROM SIR WM. TEMPLE'S COLL. BRITISH MUSEUM. COMBAT OF GREEKS AND AMAZONS.

II.—KYLIX. TWO AMAZONS CHARGING. BRITISH MUSEUM.

Facing page 144.]

nations of these women are on the south side of the river, in the province of Topago, and their chiefest strength and retreats are in the lands situate on the south side of the entrance, some sixty leagues within the mouth of the same river. The memories of the like women," adds the gallant knight, "very ancient as well in Africa as in Asia, in many histories they are verified to have been in divers ages and provinces, but they which are not far from Guiana do accompany with men but once a year, and for the time of one month, which I gather by their relations to be April. At that time all the kings of the borders assemble and the queens of the Amazons; and after the queens have chosen, the rest cast lots for their valentines. This one month they feast, dance, and drink of their wines in abundance; and the moon being done, they all depart to their own provinces. If they conceive and be delivered of a son, they return him to the father; if of a daughter, they nourish it and retain it. And as many as have daughters send unto the begetter presents, all being desirous to increase their own sex and kind; but that they cut off the right breast I do not find to be true. It was further told me that if in the wars they took any prisoners that they would accompany with those also at what time soever, but in the end for certain they put them to death; for they are said to be very cruel and bloodthirsty, especially to such as offer to invade their country. These Amazons have likewise great store of these plates of gold, which they recover in exchange chiefly for a kind of green stones, which the Spaniards call *piedras hijadas*, and we use for spleen stones: and for the disease of the stone we also esteem them. Of these

I saw divers in Guiana, and commonly every cacique has one, which their wives for the most part wear, and they esteem them as great jewels."

Then the direction again changes, and we hear of the women on the north side of the great river, retreating up the Rio Negro, ultimately hiding successfully in Guiana. Raleigh says: "On the south side of the main mouth of the Orinoco are the Arwacas, and beyond them the cannibals [Caribs], and to the south of them the Amazons." Many years after this Father Gili, writing of the Orinoco and its neighbourhood, said he closely questioned an Indian as to the surrounding tribes. Several were mentioned, and among them were the Aikeambenanoes: "Well acquainted with the Tanamac tongue," the priest declares, "I instantly comprehended the sense of the last word, which is a compound and signifies 'women living alone.'" The Indian at once confirmed his interrogator's conjecture, and giving certain details of these near yet unapproachable women, alleged that their chief industry was the making of blowpipes for the discharge of poisoned arrows in war and in the chase. When de la Condamine went through Brazil in 1745 he also questioned the natives closely as to the Amazons, and he heard of an old Indian whose father had actually conversed with "the women without husbands." On reaching the village, it was found that the old man was dead, but his son, aged apparently seventy, said that his grandfather had spoken to four Amazons, one of whom was suckling an infant at her breast, as they passed from the south side of the river to go up the valley of the Rio Negro. Another

Indian living near Para actually offered to show a river farther up which (beyond the falls in the mountain fastness) the Amazons were to be found to that day. Unfortunately, this offer does not seem to have been accepted. The upper regions of Guiana appeared to be the centre most spoken of in these days as the home of the women. Although he says, "I know that all or the greater part of the Indians of South America are liars, credulous, and enamoured of the marvellous," still de la Condamine saw no reason for scepticism, even as regards the more elaborate details of the tribe and the manner of its maintenance.

Of the origin of the "women who live without husbands" a very significant legend appears to have been current along the middle and lower reaches of the Amazon. We are told that in some far-off indeterminate age the women rebelled against their husbands and retired to the hills accompanied by only one old man. They lived by their own industry, quite isolated. All daughters born to this lopsided community were carefully reared, while all boys were killed. Then one luckless male baby, coming into the world deformed and covered with scars, called forth maternal pity. In secrecy the mother lavished all her tenderness and art in the endeavour to cure her child, but without effect until she placed him in a strongly woven bag and squeezed him into a lovely shape. Thereafter he grew apace in seclusion, day by day becoming more charming in form and character. Eventually his retreat was discovered. Then began a long and tender persecution from the women, though the boy remained unmoved. Mother and son consulted together, and to escape his tormentors the youth was thrown into the lake, where he assumed the shape of a fish. Whenever the mother called, the fish swam ashore and was instantly transformed into his beautiful human form, taking food from the hands of his mother. Jealously guarded though the secret was, feminine curiosity soon ferreted it out; and then the other women, imitating the calls, clasped the deceived young man in their arms. It was next the turn of the old man to grow uneasy, for he noticed that he was being neglected. So he set himself to watch, and the spy was driven to fierce anger by the scene of magic enacted before his eyes. His own calls to the fish were of no avail, so he made strong nets. None was stout enough, however, for always the boy-fish escaped, breaking through the meshes. The old man sat down and thought deeply, and decided upon a plan. Going to each woman of the tribe, he craftily begged them for tresses of their hair. Therewith he made a net so strong and entangling that he promptly caught and killed the fish. After this the women finally abandoned the slayer; but while he was away in his fields, his hut was always put in order by some unknown agency, and his meals prepared for him by unseen hands. So again he hid and set himself to spy. And then he saw a pet parrot fly down, put off her feathers, and swiftly change into a beautiful girl, who at once set about her duties with painstaking industry. To rush forward and fling the feathers into the fire was the work of an instant, then the watcher turned and demanded, "Who are you?" "I am," replied the mysterious squaw, "the only woman who ever loved you. Now you have broken the spell I was under, and I am glad."[1]

A variant of this is given by Barboza Rodriguez. He records a legend which shows the women as rebels against their husbands, flying to the woods, and protected in their flight by the elements and wild beasts. The men found their passage barred by flood and tempest; fierce animals fought them; monkeys gathered in the trees and pelted them with deadly missiles. So the women retired and led their own lives. Then they repented, and admitted the men to their presence once a year, giving up the boys to them, but retaining the girls. And so matters went on, until one day the whole tribe of women disappeared down a hole in the earth, led to their last resting-place by an armadillo.

It would take us too long and certainly carry us too far from our present inquiry to fully analyse each clause of these exceedingly picturesque and pregnant stories. Some points, however, may be briefly noted. In these accounts of the Amazons we have a motive for their existence introduced which is quite distinct from anything suggested by the Greeks in the case of those of Asia. In the first story, the women retiring to the hills accompanied by one old man have all the

[1] A point not noted by the American Orientalists is that Kamas, the Hindu god of love, is often shown astride a parrot, and was probably originally a parrot god. In Hindu stories the parrot constantly intervenes in amatory matters. It is curious to approach this bit of Hindu mythology with the Amazon legend and its romantic application. But for our own part we see in this only another instance of close observation of facts, in this case the peculiarly demonstrative affection most parrots have for their mates, which may even be carried further, as in the tale of the bird mourning and longing for death because the tree which had given it shelter had withered away. It is, in fact, an example of natural spontaneous symbolism.

appearance of a religious guard surrounding a priest-king. There is more than one hint of sacrifice, pre-eminently so in the case of the boy-fish, here introduced as a symbol of fertility; and finally in the most instructive version of the fable of net-entanglements—magic and woman's wiles. Hair is woman's delight and glory, but also a great means of offence. In certain cities of Asia Minor, Ashtoreth demanded the shaven head as the lesser of two personal sacrifices from her female worshippers. The Talmudists say that Lilith, the semi-human, semi-demon first wife of Adam, would, when she could, strangle the sons of men with tresses of her golden hair, out of revenge for the disinheritance of her own offspring, the Jinns. For this reason the amulet "childbirth tablets" hung on the walls of lying-in rooms of Jews both in the East and Eastern Europe always bore a representation of Lilith with an invocation for protection. But to return to our Brazilian legends. In the second, far less complicated, there is yet much that is suggestive, for here too we see the women set apart, protected supernaturally, and ending by sacrifice. For the descent into the earth means death, and its collective form and the leadership of the armadillo hints if not at the inhumation of the living, at least sacrificial burial on the death of some semi-divine chief.

It will be observed that in these two fables we are not asked to look upon the women as of a bellicose disposition—apart from their initiatory quarrel with their husbands—or as belonging to a war organisation. As a rule, however, the stories all laid stress upon their fighting qualities, and this was very persistent among the Caribs, themselves a most warlike people.

Sir Robert Schomburgk, who knew Guiana and Venezuela so well, declaring that the "Caribs are most versed in wonderful tales," disbelieved all these rumours. Of course it was impossible altogether to ignore the positive assertions of eye-witnessing Spaniards, and so, to explain these away, Sir Robert suggested that they had mistaken young men with flowing hair, and wearing necklaces and ear-rings, for women; an opinion backed up by several other authors. This is not convincing, for we must remember that Father Carbajal expressly states that the fighting women he and his companions saw had their hair twisted round their heads. A recent writer, Mr. C. R. Enoch, in his book *The Andes and the Amazon*, quotes an official Peruvian report on the native tribes inhabiting the forest regions and eastern slope of the Andes, in which the following passage occurs: "The Nahumedes are an almost extinct tribe, on the river of the same name. They are those who attacked the explorer de Orellana, who believed that these savages, with their chemises and skirts and long hair, were women warriors, or Amazons, and which name was given to the river. This must be the explanation of the supposed existence of women warriors in these regions, for no legend or history among the Indians can be found relating to any empire of women." This is an example of doubt carried to extreme limits. If the Nahumedes are the people who attacked de Orellana, they have shifted their ground considerably, which, of course, is quite possible; but it is too much to say that the Indians possess no traditions of a tribe of fighting women, in face of the legends and rumours gathered not only by such men as Father de Acuña and those more or less his contemporaries, but by such travellers as de la Condamine and others.

We do not find among early writers any claim that the female warriors were called by any local name remotely approaching that of Amazons, although these writers had always clearly in their minds the Asiatic and African stories. A recent authority, Dr. D. G. Brinton, however, has made the curious discovery that the word *amazunu* is used by the natives at the mouth of the mighty river to describe "a torrent of roaring water," and as especially applied to a bore at the outfall of the Marañon. Thereupon he suggests that the Spaniards heard this term used in reference to something wild, impetuous, and dangerous in connection with the river, and straightway evolved a non-existent tribe. It is only fair to say that there is no evidence of this in Carbajal's account or that of de Acuña. Still, it would be interesting to trace the origin of such a compound word. It is certain that the river and province was named by the Spaniards from "the Amazons made famous by historians," descendants of whom they imagined they had stumbled upon, and not from any chance name uttered by the Indians. Is it possible that the compound word is, after all, of later date than the Spanish Conquest and the renaming of the river? Such tricks of philology are by no means uncommon.

As late as 1743, when de la Condamine was travelling through the country, rumours about the Amazons still persisted, but, like de Acuña, de Ribera, Gili, and many more, this worthy explorer never caught a glimpse of them or the mysterious Manoa. He could only meet people who said they had seen them in some remote, ill-defined region, and who knew others who had years before visited the women and country, which, however, could never be located. When de la Condamine was making his inquiries, it was said that the Amazons had moved off up the Rio Negro, and they continued to retreat before the inquisitive whites into the unmapped forest regions of Guiana. Humboldt, like de la Condamine, was a strong believer in the tales, though his investigations were as little conclusive. Sceptics were equally numerous, and some had made their voices heard even in the days of the conquistadors. There were those ready to insist that the legend grew from the crafty designs of de Orellana, who wished by these devious means to wipe out the memory of his gross treachery to his chief Pizarro, thinking that by marvellous accounts of his own exploits he would wrest applause and rewards from those at home. It is scarcely necessary to attribute wilful intention to mislead on the part of Father Carbajal and other explorers on this head. That women did appear in arms in America as well as in Asia, and for the matter of that in Europe too, there is no reason to doubt. Many instances may be cited.

Juan de lo Cosa reported that when he sailed with Rodrigo de Bastides in 1501 he landed with a party far north of the Orinoco on the site now occupied by Cartagena, and he and his party were boldly attacked by men and women who mingled in the fight, both sexes wielding most dexterously the long dart, or azagay, and bow with poisoned arrows. Hulderick Schnirdel, who travelled in company with Spaniards through the country of the River

Plate and the Amazon between the years 1534 and 1554, heard much of the fighting Amazons, who were said to live in an island, to have no silver or gold, which they left with their husbands on the mainland—altogether a novel account. Schnirdel went in search of the island, but fruitlessly. He doubted that a nation existed, though he attests that the fighting of women in the ranks with their menkind was common enough. A little later, in 1587, Lopez Vaz recounts the adventures of Lopez de Agira. This de Agira was the rebel and renegade who murdered Don Fernando de Gusman, who had proclaimed himself Emperor of Peru. After the murder, de Agira, accompanied by a few soldiers and natives, started down the Amazon *en route* for the Atlantic. They met with some opposition, and found it was true that Amazons existed—"that is to say, women who fight in the wars with bows and arrows; but these women fight to aid their husbands, and not by themselves alone without companies of men, as de Orellana reports. There were of these women upon divers parts of the river, who, seeing Spaniards fighting with their husbands, came in to succour them, and showed themselves more valiant than their husbands." But the comparative rarity of the phenomena would be sufficient to stir the imagination of the Spaniards, whose minds, as we have said, were stored with stories of the classic period and tales of the East.

The early Spanish critics accepted the story of the fighting women, as evidence to this effect accumulated, while more or less politely disbelieving the story of Amazon "nations," and their arguments are based on the very fact that women fight side by side with their husbands, and that such-like warrior women were well known both in ancient and modern history. It must also be remembered that America was still part of the Indies to most of the early explorers, and to them it seemed quite natural that the famous Themysciran nation should have migrated farther afield. It followed that these explorers should find that these warrior women were white, for so the fitness of things demanded, though there is a possible explanation for a light-coloured band of women if we suppose them to have belonged to a semi-religious caste. Then there was another school, holding that this nation of women was the remnant of those who had escaped from Asia through Africa by way of Hesperides or the lost Atlantis. To most of the travellers, as with Father de Acuña, the "Amazons made famous by historians," or, in other words, the Asiatic dames, could not be forgotten, and the stories of fabulous wealth could only contribute to their belief.

Down to quite recent times there were persistent rumours of wonderful cities hidden away in almost impenetrable forests, stored with great treasures of gold, and often said to be guarded by women, though we see from Schnirdel's report that the office of treasure-guardianship might be reversed. The typical examples were the phantom cities of Dobayba, where there existed a golden temple to a Nature goddess, and Manoa del Dorado, so constantly talked about as near at hand, but never seen: the latter a city with houses roofed with gold, bathed by a crystal-clear lake, the waters rippling over sands of gold. Now, in justification of this, we may point out that when the Spaniards came to Peru for the second time, and made the unfortunate Emperor Atahualpa prisoner in his own castle of Cajamarca, the Inca offered as a ransom to fill a room, said to be 22 feet by 27 feet, as high as he could reach, say 6 feet, with gold. This, it has been estimated, would have amounted to a value of a hundred million sterling. But the Spaniards were impatient, and slaughtered their prisoner, a proceeding indefensible on moral grounds, and as a matter of policy less sensible than killing the goose that laid the golden eggs. The treasure was never forthcoming. Yet at Cuzco, the true capital of the Inca power, and at Pachacamac, the Spaniards found the palace walls covered with plates of gold. Offerings of gold chains and flowers of golden plates also seem to have been thrown into lakes. At the birth of the last undoubted heir of the Incas, who received the symbolic name of Huasca, "The Chain," or "The Cable," a commemorative chain said to be 233 yards long and composed of heavy links of gold was made and cast into Lake Orcos, no doubt as a thanksoffering.

That the sands of lakes and rivers abounded in alluvial deposits of finely powdered gold is true to this day as it was of old. Stories of such richly endowed cities were not confined to Brazil and Peru, but were common to Guiana, Honduras, and so on. The grounds for these legends were perfectly natural, as we have just shown. Besides, many of the most wonderful buildings of the Incas, Aztecs, and others were placed either in most difficultly accessible mountains, or on islands in big lakes, or in dense forests. Von Hassell in 1905 explored much of the upper reaches of the Amazon on the Atlantic side of the Cordilleras, and he visited the great fluvial island of Tumpinambaranas, where he found stupendous ruins, reminding him of the civilisation of the Incas. He says that the Amazon plain must have been visited by repeated waves of emigrants, having civilisation as advanced as that of the Incas, but who had disappeared, leaving faint traces behind them. Baron Nordenskold, on his travels in Chaco, in Argentina, "found large places in the primeval forests beyond the real Calchaqui territory, in districts at present very sparsely inhabited."

The Toltec city of Quiché, capital of Utatlan, Central America, apparently had a population of 3,000,000, and the Spaniards' description of the Royal Palace reads like an account of the Alhambra in its days of glory. Experience taught that it was customary for people threatened with invasion to remove their treasures to as inaccessible retreats as possible, where, also, the womenfolk would be gathered, and these, in default of men, would as occasion demanded take part in the defence of their lares and penates. Villages, too, were often occupied by women, old men, and young children alone for many weeks together, while the men and youths were away on the war-path or some great hunting expedition. Moreover, in this part of the American continent, where moon-worship prevailed, there were certain ceremonies connected with womanhood and child-bearing involving the separation of women from all males, and apparently elaborate dances in the moonlight. Upon these solid enough foundations the Spaniards, by frequently injudicious questioning of the natives, built up a rickety superstructure of many strange fables. The evil practice of our own Counsels learned in the law have taught us the very real danger of putting leading questions, even when addressed to educated people able to grasp their meaning. But when you have a credulous cross-examiner, bewildered by the novelty of his surroundings, his head stuffed full with the stories from Quintus Curtius and Diodorus the Sicilian, and on the other hand a horde of naked savages, or even of semi-barbarians, catching most imperfectly at the meaning of their questioners, it will be readily seen that the answers easily took the form that the interlocutor more or less unconsciously desired.

That women did fight on occasion—and this would be particularly true of the hill and forest tribes—we have already seen by various travellers' accounts. That they were occasionally for a length of several moons a tribe, as it were, by themselves, and guardians of tribal treasures, there is no reason to disbelieve. Ample material here for a very robust and circumstantial legend, without either party to the making thereof being liars of malice aforethought.

An extraordinary fact, which should be mentioned in this place, as it may have some bearing on the subject, is that the Lenâpé tribe of North American Indians were called "Women." They were a branch of the great Algonkin nation, but found themselves down in Delaware, surrounded by the warlike Iroquois. That they could boast of an honourable origin is proved by the fact that the three Delaware sub-tribes had as their totems the tortoise (above all honoured as the servant of the All-Powerful Creator, and on whose back the earth was built up), the wolf, and the turkey. Moreover, Dr. Brinton informs us that Lenâpé means "men of our nation," or "our men." Yet it appears that for a lengthy period this tribe never went to war, and although in later years apparently not held in high esteem, unquestionably filled an important office as a kind of buffer nation of peacemakers. Among most American tribes there existed a Council of Women, composed of the old matrons, whose privilege it was to meet in war-time and discuss matters affecting the tribe. If they advocated peace, it was no disgrace for the "braves" to listen to them and consider the advisability of offering terms to the enemy. It was in some such position as this that the whole tribe of Delaware Algonkins were placed. According to their own statements, the Lenâpés became the peacemaking tribe at the special request of the Iroquois, who saw that the nations were eating each other up. So they approached the Lenâpés with an honourable proposition, and in the presence of the other assembled tribes gave the Delawares the long robe and ear-rings of women, so that they should not bear arms or mingle in strife; the calabash of oil and medicine, to the end that they might become the nurses; the corn pestle and hoe, so that they might cultivate the land; and, in order to emphasise the whole solemnity, bestowed on the chiefs of the "Women" tribe a belt of wampum, the greatest of symbols of peace and fraternity within their gift, as each division of the strange ceremony was reached. That the Lenâpés fulfilled their mission seems certain, although as time went on the Iroquois began to treat them as a conquered tribe, and used the term "Women" as applied to them with some contumely. This buffer tribe, with its claims to a high mission and its equivocal position and attributes, appears to be unique in American Indian social economy; on the other hand, at all events in the southern part of the continent, there were classes of men in the barbarian nations dressed and treated as women. The whole problem of the "Women" tribe, however, is far from being cleared up. Was it cajoled into its curious place as the result of some dim recollection of a once-powerful women-priest caste? Or was it merely a clever device suggested by pressing needs when it began to be recognised that there must be occasional cessation from the interminable intertribal slaughter? It is a mystery full of suggestion.

To most, if not to all, of the tales that the Spaniards gave a willing credence there was a solid substratum of truth. The splendid build of the Caribs, the abnormal proportions of the men down in the terrible Tierra del Fuego, and the dwarfish tribes of the forest regions and of the degenerate Aztecs, would account for the giants and pigmies of whom so much was heard. In such matters the terms are essentially comparative to both questioner and questioned, and, moreover, the "little men" term may be relative not only to their

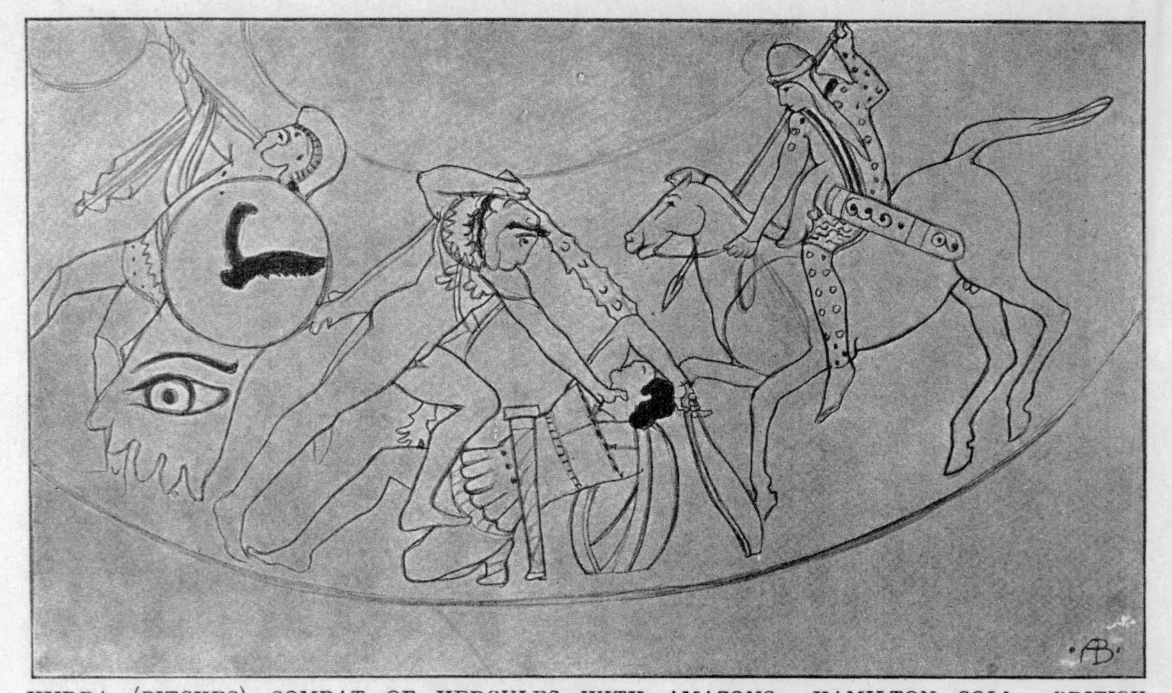

HYDRA (PITCHES) COMBAT OF HERCULES WITH AMAZONS. HAMILTON COLL. BRITISH MUSEUM.

Facing page 161.]

stature but to moral qualities also. To the hard-fighting, hungry Carib the man of peace was unquestionably a "little man" no matter how tall or broad-shouldered he might be, just as to-day in the East the mass of people without influence are "little men" to the rulers and their satellites. Even the men with their toes pointing the wrong way (of whom the world had heard before from the early Greek writers on India) existed, for the reversing of moccasins or other feet-covering is a natural dodge adopted to bewilder, and the attempted explanation of such a trick would be quite sufficient to make confusion worse confounded.

Nor need we have a moment's hesitation in crediting the existence of tailed tribes, for totemism and the respect that comes of fear inspired by wild horned beasts was quite sufficient to make man proud of caudal appendages and to supply his own deficiencies in this matter. Even Hercules so managed the draping of the lion's skin about his own body as to secure a very fine tail. Dionysus also treated his panther's skin in the same way, while his Seleni sported the tails of giddy goats with waggish effrontery. In most parts of Africa the buffalo's tail is an emblem of power, as the horse's tail is in Northern Africa and Arabia, whether carried in the hand or worn pendant behind from the waist, the latter method of personal adornment applying to the buffalo's tail, and is found to prevail in the south, east, and west.

Lord Hindlip, writing of the Kavirondo tribes in British East Africa, says the women are fond of a certain amount of adornment, and that "a peculiar ornament is a grass tail tied round the waist generally by a string of beads. I believe," he adds, "that this is an emblem of marriage, and to touch one of those tails is a breach of good manners, the offender being liable to a fine of five goats." Bruce and Baker also mention women in the far Sudan and in the Upper Nile Valley wearing tails of plaited skin or of string. In North America certain ceremonials include the Buffalo Dance, when every "brave" carries horns on his head and a tail waggles fiercely in the rear during the saltatory performance. Both the men and women of the Aymara Indians of Peru and Bolivia wear their hair long and plaited into tails, hence it was supposed that they had originally emigrated from China, or at least been influenced by a Chinese invasion prior to the Inca era. To all these, tails are of no small importance, and would be looked upon by their neighbours with awe or contempt according to tribal relations.

It is in this spirit that most of the Amazon stories must be treated. At the same time, we must not omit to quote some weighty opinions pointing to a more direct acceptation. De la Condamine, who was a thoroughgoing believer in the American Amazon nation, argued that its evolution was quite natural and a development for which we might have looked with confidence. He held that the women leading migratory lives, often following their husbands to war, were usually compelled to submit to very harsh domestic conditions. But the very conditions imposed upon them by their mode of life afforded ample opportunities for them to escape from the tyranny by simply detaching themselves from the tribe and forming a community wherein, if they did not exactly gain independence, they would no longer be slaves and beasts of burden. This method of establishing new communities was, he pointed out, going on in every colony where slave-holding was tolerated; the slaves growing tired of ill-treatment escaped to the forests or swamps, setting up their own camps and villages. Robert Southey re-echoed this opinion that "the lot of women is usually dreadful among savages. . . . Had we never heard of the Amazons of antiquity, I should, without hesitation, believe in those of America." To him the terrible hardships of the Indian women's lives demanded some such relief, and he looked upon the existence of such communities as redounding to the credit of humanity, showing that there was hope for its regeneration. A recent writer of deep philosophic tendencies, Mr. E. J. Payne, follows on the same lines. He regards the whole phenomena of Amazonian states as a perfectly legitimate and understandable outcome of the transition from savagery to barbarism, a period when life is peculiarly harsh to womankind. But, as he says, such communities always carry within themselves the seeds of decay, for they cannot extend, cannot indeed exist for long, without the tolerance of man. A day comes when he grows tired of a complacent attitude, and the women then have nothing to do but surrender on his own terms. These are undoubtedly both interesting and plausible theories, which do not really enter into conflict with the opinions that we have ventured to advance on the whole subject.

CHAPTER IX

The Amazon Stones

An outstanding fact connected with the traditions of Amazons in South America is that most travellers refer, like Sir Walter Raleigh and de la Condamine, to certain greenstones, some form of jade, which the Indians were understood to declare they obtained from "the women who live without husbands." De la Condamine saw many of these stones in different parts of the country, and always received the same explanation as to their origin. They were either roughly wrought in the shape of birds or beasts, or formed into bead-like cylinders two to three inches long, both smooth and in some cases richly carved with curious designs of the intricate, involved kind we associate with Aztec art. Almost always these were pierced longitudinally with round holes, and were worn pendant from the neck as precious talismans, in the sense mentioned by Raleigh.

These quaint relics, common to the whole of South America and Mexico, and of which the natives gave such a mysterious account, helped to bolster up an elaborate theory, over which archæologists and anthropologists have long wrangled. It was contended that jade was an Oriental stone, and that, moreover, the carvings found on these amulets, cylindrical or otherwise, bore a distinctly Oriental character. Thereupon was built up a voluminous body of evidence tending to show that the Aztecs of Mexico, the mysterious inhabitants of Yucatan, the Incas of Peru, and, we may add, the Amazons of Brazil, came from Asia. This, of course, was backed up by arguments based on the similarity of symbols (such as the cross, the tau, and the cramponed cross or swaticha), the approximation of various customs (human sacrifices to sun and moon, women priests and eunuchs as ministrants in monolithic temples), and certain supposed identical points in anthropology. As a matter of fact, however, the similarity is more apparent than real; there is a certain superficial resemblance, but the divergencies as regards the use of symbols and as to the customs appear too great for these to be attributed merely to influences resulting from migrations to new surroundings. Rather does this similarity prove that after all human nature is very human, and that wants and desires, physical and intellectual, are likely to manifest themselves in ways that approach uniformity in their broad outlines.

As regards the matter immediately under discussion, the greenstones, it is clear that they vary considerably in their substance, the amulets consisting of true jade (a silicate of lime and magnesia), jadeite (a silicate of sodium and aluminium), feldspathic rock, and quartz. In any case, there was no need to go to Asia for the stones, as both jade and jadeite are sufficiently abundant and widely distributed over Central and South America, though, it is true, are not easily found. That the art of polishing and carving such stones, which are usually extremely tough and generally hard enough to resist the file, was a lost one when the Spaniards arrived on the scene, is quite true; but then so much connected with ancient and the comparatively recent civilisation of those countries had so utterly disappeared that we must not be astonished at the loss of this finer phase of the lapidary's skill. Instances of such losses in arts are only too common in every period and every country. Even to go no farther than Peru, we find that the Incas once possessed the secret of polishing emeralds and piercing them with circular holes without damaging the gems—certainly a more difficult task than dealing with jade or quartz. Many other local examples of this passing away of specialised skill could be enumerated.

It is apparent, from what Sir Walter Raleigh and others say, that these shaped, and mostly graven, greenstones were looked upon as talismans of fertility, just in the same light as flint arrow-heads were practically all the world over, not only from China to Peru, but from the African forests to the dales of Cumberland. But while flints—held to be thunderbolts, and therefore associated with storm-clouds and the life-giving showers accompanying them, the fertilising gifts of the gods—had a general application to vegetation, and usually also to cattle, the greenstones were particularly connected with child-bearing. There is a great deal of most fascinating, even instructive, mythology attached to all this (instructive, because not altogether devoid of a foundation based on observed fact), which was far spread over the face of the inhabited globe.

It was generally recognised that the showers accompanying thunderstorms were most beneficial to vegetation, though it was reserved for the nineteenth century to find at least a partial explanation in the fact that a discharge of electricity in the air has the effect of fixing free nitrogen, which is washed down by the rain to form plant food. No doubt jade is held in exceptionally high honour in every part of the East, though perhaps most markedly so in China, but the cult for this stone and its congeners extended far beyond the Orient. Personal ornaments made of them are still largely worn by women, in the form of bracelets, necklets, and pendant-amulets. By a not very recondite association of ideas we find such stones also appreciated by men—the Turks, for instance, being fond of having their sword hilts (and the sword is the professional fighter's *alta ego*, the symbol of his strength, even his representative, as we see in so many forms of ceremonial) made of jade. In other directions the stones, by an equally comprehensible association of ideas, were worn as amulets against painful renal disorders.

In New Zealand the Maoris place great store on their grotesquely carved breast greenstone pendants, which are like those of Brazil, made of jade, jadeite, or other similarly coloured stones. In various parts of Europe, too, especially in France and Switzerland, jade amulets and arrow-heads have been found, to a large extent among remains connected with the lacustrine races. As was the case with the American amulets, it was long held that these European ornaments must have come from Asia, because no natural deposits of the stone had been traced; but closer investigation has resulted in the recognition of jadeite, and perhaps also jade, pebbles in the Swiss rivers, which must have been washed down from hidden sources, while Saussure, and others after him, discovered a variety of jade, which has been named saussurite, *in situ* among the Swiss Alps. More generous deposits of true nephrite have also come to light in North-Eastern Europe. All these stones are of a yellowish green hue, are semi-transparent, and have a greasy feel: it was these characteristics that made them particularly prized. But the same circle of ideas is associated with most green and blue stones. Indeed, green and blue are the symbolic colours in this respect. Blue represents the vault of heaven, the world beyond—therefore faith; green stands for deep water, vegetation, spring—therefore life and hope. This pertains to the universals of symbolism. In Central America they are connected with the "Feathered Serpent," the "Engendering" manifestation of the Supreme Being, who is enveloped in blue and green (the sky and vegetation), and is called the Heart of the Lake, the Master of the Blue Depths—which is particularly significant when we come to consider how the Amazons are said to have obtained the fertilising amulets by diving into moonlit lakes.

In the Bible this colour symbolism, and often associated with precious stones, is general. Both in Exodus and Ezekiel the foundation of God's throne rests on the dark blue firmament with its golden stars, which is compared to a floor inlaid with sapphires. In this connection the sapphire must be translated as lapis-lazuli, a deep blue stone sprinkled with spots of iron pyrites which glitter like the twinkling of stars. The rainbow about the throne is compared to an emerald. In the prophetic description of the New Jerusalem of the twelve encircling walls the fifth is founded on beryl, the sixth on turquoise, the eighth on sapphire, the ninth on emerald, the tenth on chrysolite, the eleventh on topaz, and the twelfth on amethyst. The gates are made of sapphire. Then again, the sapphire is used figuratively in the description of the human body, and probably referred to the blue veins. Of the twelve stones in the breastplate of the High Priest, two-thirds are either blue or green: there is the pale yellow-green topaz, the green emerald, the blue gold-splashed lapis-lazuli, the red-green yashefeh, the sky-blue agate, the bluish violet amethyst, the bright green malachite, the yellowish verging to dark blue yahalom. It is curious to note that the Cabalists held the sapphire to be fatal to serpents, while the Talmudists declared that the sapphire on the High Priest's breastplate was engraved by a worm.

According to the Talmudists, the Tables of the Law were of sapphire, which probably also means lapis-lazuli. Many of the temple dedication inscriptions from Asia Minor are on this beautiful stone. The true sapphire is "the stone of chastity," which dispelled bad dreams, preserved the sight; while in China the star variety is regarded as a love charm. In India the star sapphire is said to be the daughter of Brahma's tears. This is all the more interesting as it is connected with the universal belief in the necessity of suffering and sacrifice for the redemption of mankind. Legend says that Brahma the Creator, being anxious to sympathise with man and to set an example of self-sacrifice, sinned; and so bitter was his feeling thereupon that a tear gathered in his eye and fell to the earth in the form of a star sapphire. Thus the gem is the symbol of the repentant sinner, of sacrifice hallowed. The amethyst was "the maid stone"; it possessed the virtue of detecting poisons, and therefore the cups out of which mythical god-heroes drank were carved out of amethyst. When engraved with symbols of the moon and tied round the neck by hair, the stones became talismans against witchcraft. The turquoise brought good luck. So did the emerald, especially in love affairs: it changed colour if the donor proved false, detected treachery generally, restored the sight, cured epilepsy, and was the great amulet for procuring easy child-birth.

Generally speaking, the sapphire symbolises the azure of the sky—therefore religious hope; the emerald, vegetation, spring, Venus, love.[1] So we find, according to tradition, Pope Innocent III. sending to King John of England four rings: the sapphire to represent hope; the emerald, faith; the garnet, charity; and the topaz, good works—of all of which he stood much in need. The Cabalists prepared planetary rings as follows: for Mars, the emerald set in iron; for Venus, the amethyst set in copper; for Saturn, the turquoise set in lead;

[1] In heraldry azure is represented by the sapphire or by the zodiacal sign for Jupiter; vert (green) by the emerald, or the sign of Venus; purpure (purple) by the amethyst, or the sign of Mercury.

for the sun, the sapphire set in gold. Their special symbolism was probably derived from the Arabian authors.

Jade itself derives its name of nephrite from its supposed beneficial influence on renal diseases, so that the Spaniards, doubtless in this following the Indians, called the South America cylinders *piedras hijados*, or loin stones. A Cabalistic formula for the use of jade, coming to us by way of Egypt, says that the stone should be formed into a perfect square, marked with the numerals 1. 8. 1. 1, set in pure gold, and then breathed upon three times at dawn and sunset, repeating the word "Thoth" five hundred times, and finally the whole has to be tied round with a red thread (the thread of life). The result was a talisman which ensured to the possessor success in all things, for nobody could say him "Nay," no matter what favour or service he might crave. Thoth, of course, is the great ibis-headed moon-god of the Upper Nile, who was adorned with a crescent, and recorded the judgments given in the Nether World by Osiris. Hence those who possessed "Words of Power" could convert certain bones of the sacred ibis into "wish-bones," by holding which any strong desire would be fulfilled. Thoth was in a sense the Mercury of the Egyptian gods, the inventor of letters, and, by reason of his assistance to widowed Isis and orphaned Horus the Younger from the persecution of the elder or Solar Horus, became protector of infants. He was the god amidst the rushes, where he hid Horus; and so the ibis may be compared to the baby-bringing storks of folklore.

Now, in the Aztec heavenly economy Tlaloc is "The Wine of the Earth," a powerful god whose consort, Chalchihuitlicue, "She of the Emerald Robes," is protectress of lakes and running water. Her symbols are the green jade and the emerald, hence called chalchihuitl. This reminds us of the Hindu goddess Durga, also a fertility divinity, "Granter of Boons," "Giver of Victory in Battle," who is invoked as "Wearer of Bangles of Emeralds and Sapphires," "Resplendent with Peacocks' Feathers erect on the Head." The son of Tlaloc and Chalchihuitlicue is Quetzalcoatl, a most austere member of the pantheon, yet to whom thanksgiving was offered on the birth of any child, such child being acclaimed in the religious invocation as "precious gem, emerald, sapphire, beauteous feather . . . formed in the ninth heaven . . . where his divine majesty fashioned you in a mould, as one fashions a ball of gold; you have been chiselled as a precious stone."

Of course this beautiful idea of a babe being fashioned in heaven is not peculiar to Central America any more than is connecting green and blue stones with love and child-bearing, but it will be seen that in the Mexico of the Aztecs every child was indeed Dieudonné. Quetzalcoatl was regarded as the inventor of the art of cutting and polishing precious stones, and was patron of lapidaries as well as protector of all new-born babies. Now, the Indians of Brazil declared that the Amazons obtained their treasured amulets from a lake close to Jamunda, a high mountain near the supposed original site of Manoa del Dorado. The Amazons gathered together by night, and, having ceremonially purified themselves, worshipped the moon, invocating her as the Mother of the Greenstones. Then, when the moon was reflected on the waters, they plunged into the lake, and received the stones from the goddess. Moon-worship was general in the plains of the Amazon. She was the creator of all plants, especially of maize; her subject gods were the increscent and decrescent moons, each of which ruled over minor gods, who were the *geni loci* of woods, glens, mountains, streams, and lakes, which is the crude form of the belief we have seen existed in Mexico. A curious variant of the story of the capture of the greenstones says that these were alive, swimming about in the lake like fishes, and could not be caught until the Amazons had made personal sacrifice by cutting themselves, when a drop of blood falling over the wriggling green jade acted magically, the stones remaining quiet and allowing themselves to be caught. At this stage they were said to be soft and plastic; the Amazons took them and with their hands shaped them in the rays of the moon, after which they gradually hardened. These stories, while they connect the greenstones with the heavenly queen, who sent down the vivifying dew and soft light, also seem to bear witness to the difficulty of securing jade or jadeite, which was perhaps but rarely discovered *in situ*, being mostly derived from erratic blocks and water-borne pebbles.

As regards the malleability of stones, it is interesting to find traditions in Peru that the Incas possessed the secret of softening stones with some potent herbal preparation, facilitating the moulding of huge blocks and quaint carvings characteristic of their great buildings, often erected on high and almost inaccessible mountains. Some stones are soft and easily worked when freshly extracted from deep quarries, while lava from active volcanoes is capable of being cut and even moulded; but the stones under discussion, the huge monoliths of the Inca buildings, do not belong to either of these classes. On the other hand, it is probable that jade is really softer when freshly mined, gradually hardening on exposure: several recent observers in Eastern Europe have declared this to be a fact. Then de la Condamine, reporting the traditions of the Brazilian natives, says: "It is seriously asserted that this stone was nothing else than the mud of the river, which, when recently taken from the bed, might be moulded into any form, and which obtained its extreme hardness by exposure to the air." The association of ideas running through these myths and legends is certainly remarkable. That the greenstones had been formed by pressing ooze from river-beds was a belief quite commonly held, and, of course, the mere failure to reproduce the miracle was no proof of error to the native mind, the essential something, the magic touch and incantations, being absent in the case of the experimenters. Digging up of ooze from beneath the waters in order to obtain life is a widespread belief, and may be compared with the Greek legends and the theories of modern evolutionists. The Algonkins, to mention one among many instances, say that in the beginning of things the world was a waste of waters, and thereon floated a raft loaded with animals, the king of whom was the Great White

Rabbit (or the Hare). There was no place whereon these animals could rest their feet in comfort, and the Great White Rabbit called upon the amphibious creatures to dive in search of earth. Down went the beaver, but he came up after a long time exhausted and unsuccessful. Then the otter dived, with no better result. So the musk-rat offered her services. Though the probability of succour from so insignificant a creature seemed small, she was allowed to try. The musk-rat disappeared, and remained under water for so long that she was mourned as dead. Suddenly she floated up, apparently lifeless, but in one of her tiny paws was a little mud. This the Great White Rabbit proceeded to mould, and as he worked it grew in volume. A great island was formed, with its plains and mountains, which continued to increase as the White Rabbit walked round and round, pressing and shaping. The land grew so much that it afforded a home for the animals, but it was quite barren. Then the Great White Rabbit shot flints into the earth, and these sprouted into trees and brought forth vegetation of every description. Still there was no human life, but the White Rabbit created men and women from dead animals. Hence, according to many, arose the complicated law of totems, which on the one hand touches universalism, uniting humanity with the whole animate and inanimate world, and on the other leads to endless differentiation.

A similar idea was at the back of the Hebrew tradition relating to the creation of Adam. The Talmudists say that God sent Gabriel, Michael, and Israfel to fetch seven separate handfuls of earth for the formation of the first man, the earth to be from different depths and of different colours (hence, say some, the origin of the various races and their distinctive hues); but the Earth, fearing that man would be bad and bring disgrace upon her, pleaded against the Divine design, and each angel, touched by her arguments, returned empty-handed. Then Asrael descended and performed the task, and was commanded henceforth to separate the souls from the bodies, so he was called the Angel of Death. The Hebrew Doctors add that of the seven handfuls that taken from Babylonia went to form the most honoured parts of Adam.

Thus do we see the Indians of the North and the South, the Aztecs of Mexico, and the wonderful Semitic "Chosen People" bringing the vasty deep, the earth, and the limitless heavens together, and finding a place for man in their cosmogonies. One dominant fact in all this is that Nature is nothing without the creative power of the Spirit. Water and earth bring forth, but they are only fruitful through the intervention of the spiritual, manifested in certain cases by such forces as the sun, moon, and wind, which animate indeed, but merely as the instruments of a Creative Force outside of Nature. The whole range of the symbolism of colour and gems illustrates the belief in this great unfathomable secret of life.

I.—AMAZONS FROM DEINOS (BOWL).
II.—COMBAT OF AMAZONS WITH ATHIC HEROES (BRITISH MUSEUM).
III.—AMAZON CHARGING FROM KYLIX (BRITISH MUSEUM).
IV.—CAMEOS IN BRITISH MUSEUM.
V.—HEADS OF AMAZONS, SARDONY X (FROM BLARAS COLLECTION).

Facing page 176

CHAPTER X

Conclusion

Even when divested of adventitious adornments, there remains a remarkable body of evidence as to the widely prevailing belief in the existence of countries, districts, or islands populated solely by women. Such a phenomenon cannot be entirely ignored by the student of human nature, and is, indeed, worthy of some painstaking inquiry. From the very outset it is clear that the Greek myth is not sufficient to account for all the stories, though it is, of course, indisputable that these legends have largely coloured most of the tales that have reached us. But that narrow and somewhat egoistic view which sought to trace back everything to Grecian influence is quite inadequate to explain the traditions found to exist in every quarter of the globe. We cannot admit the theory that these legends or customs have been spread by migrations. Nor can we accept the ideas put forward by Robert Southey, Sir Clement Markham, and Mr. E. J. Payne to the effect that the hardships imposed on women in savagedom caused revolts resulting in the formation of feminine "tribes," living apart, fighting, and only having voluntary intercourse with men, as an all-embracing explanation. We must seek deeper than such theories as these will take us.

It is possible to divide roughly the legends and traditions into three main classes. We have: (1) Women living apart in colonies, but having occasional communications with the outside world on a peaceful footing. (2) Women banded together as a fighting organisation. (3) Nations ruled over by queens, and mainly, or to a considerable extent, governed by women. Varied as are the stories which we have reviewed in the foregoing chapters, it will be seen that they all fall into one or other of these divisions. Now, if we examine the matter, we shall see that all three are simple outcomes of different stages in social evolution. Of course, we find them often profoundly modified by local conditions. They are so far healthful signs inasmuch as they are different manifestations of life rather than of stagnation, showing a striving after some form of ideal, however benighted, amidst the discomforts of periods of transition. We may see the three stages following each other, by no means always in the same sequence: a hyper-cultivation of one phase or another, frequent blendings, and much irregularity of survival. Which is quite what might be expected if we accustom ourselves to look upon the phenomena as usually the spontaneous outcome of local needs.

It must be admitted that as society emerges from savagedom into barbarism on the road towards civilisation, the burthens of the respective sexes are readjusted, and not without considerable friction and discomfort. Man ceases to be merely a fighting and hunting animal; he becomes the larder-filler in a wider sense. Now, this often involved, and, indeed, does still involve, gathering harvests and collecting foods or food values of one kind or another far from home. Sometimes the whole tribe will move from winter to summer quarters with this object in view. We find this typified in its most exaggerated form by the nomadic communities. But to go no great distance, we find this kind of thing largely prevailing to this day in Switzerland, in Norway, in certain parts of Italy and Corsica, chiefly, though not entirely, among shepherds and cattle-keeping folk. But often enough it is the men alone, with the growing lads, who go off on active work, leaving the homes to the safe-keeping of the women, with a sprinkling of old men and small boys. Corsica offers a curious combination of phenomena bearing on this point. First, we find that there is a winter migration of the shepherd people from the interior to the coast villages, and a summer migration away from the malarious coast to the mountain villages and grassy slopes, which often leads to a strange numerical inequality of the sexes in the different villages. Secondly, the island is annually invaded by a swarm of Italian able-bodied men and youths, chiefly from the districts surrounding Lucca, who come to till the vineyards and do other heavy agricultural work which the native Corsican deems beneath his dignity. Thousands of the Lucchessi come, generally in squads of five, remain for about three months, and then return to their homes. They invariably arrive without their womankind, so that their villages practically become feminine communities during these regularly recurring periods of absence.

A similar state of affairs is known to have existed among many tribes of the Caucasus. Quite late in the day Father Lamberti found that the Suani men, a brave, strongly built mountain tribe, and extremely poor, came down every summer to work in the plains at the foot of the Caucasus, taking back to their families in their isolated homes food, copper, and certain other raw materials for their modest industrial enterprises. Fishing as an industry frequently leads to the same conditions; indeed, even now during the herring season temporary feminine communities are formed on the coast of Scotland by the fish-cleaners, who remain hard at work dealing with the catches between the visits of the fleets. It is some such natural explanation that occurs in regard to Marco Polo's story of the Male and Female isles, thus coinciding also with what we gather from Lord Macartney's account of the Zaporavna Cossacks and the Dnieper island. We can easily understand that such conditions, if accentuated beyond the ordinary course owing to local exigencies, would give rise to misapprehension among the ill-informed, or among people of other ways of living, who are by habit of thought and actual training intolerant of any divergence from the normal.

Then, again, these conditions, which exist chiefly among communities living in mountainous districts, forests, and small islands, would lead to developments in other directions. The women would of necessity cultivate the arts of governance and of warfare, for obviously the maleless villages would be more open to attack, and would often call for not merely bravery on the part of the women, but of cunning in the method of defence and counter-attack. Something of this conflict of sentiment and method is revealed to us by

Quintus Smyrnus in his account of the struggle between the Greeks and Amazons before Troy. The warrior feeling is expressed by Hippodamia, who, excited by the brave deeds of Penthesilea and her companions, calls upon the Trojan maids andmatrons—

> "Come, friends, let us too in our hearts conceive
> A martial spirit such as now inflames
> Our warriors fighting for their native walls;
> For not in strength are we inferior much
> To men; the same our eyes, our limbs the same;
> One common light we see, one air we breathe;
> Nor different is the food we eat. What then
> Denied to us hath Heaven on man bestowed?
> O let us hasten to the glorious war!"

But Theano, "for her prudence famed," deprecates such a move—

> "Till the foe hath closely girt our towers
> We shall not need the aid of female hands."

Which shows how old these ever-new problems are. Forgotten for a season, they are rediscovered and proclaimed as startling novelties or divine revelations, only to be inevitably brought within the compass of reason by the hard logic of facts, and the Theanos prevails.

No doubt in certain stages of society the whole tribe moves, and the women, especially if of a hardy mountain or forest stock, would naturally share all forms of activity with the men within the measure of their strength, and the more skilful of them would be found in the fighting ranks with the male warriors. Thus it comes about that historians and travellers tell us now of unisex organisations, and then of women—in Asia, Europe, Africa, and America—using the bow and arrow, the sling and the lance, aiding and abetting their husbands and brothers in martial exploits.

As we have in effect already observed, the *juste milieu* is never a strong point in feminine nature, and so fighting woman becomes in very deed an "unholy terror," something particularly abhorrent to those who are fresh from casting off the fetters of barbarism. The ratio between fighting men and women would constantly vary under the influence of seasons or tribal evolution, and so tend to further accentuate error of judgment, giving rise to robust myths.

Great, too, is the influence of religious ideas. Marco Polo says that the dwellers in his dual islands observed the ordinances of the Old Testament. This segregation of women during periods of childbirth may be traced as having been a matter of common occurrence in all times and places. We have much evidence of this among the Hebrews and their neighbours, and also in modern times among races far apart. The Toda dairy folk of the Nilgeri Hills, whose most strange pre-nuptial custom is extremely suggestive of ceremonies attending the worship of Astarte of old and of the Indian goddesses Kali and Durgan to this day, build special huts for expectant mothers, such huts being placed away from the villages and all paths used by man and the sacred herds. They may not join the community again until after having undergone a purificatory ceremony. So too with the Waiknas of the Mosquito coast, a retreat being "prepared for them in the depths of the woods, where they are not allowed to emerge for a stated period—that accomplished, a public lustration of mother and infant takes place." Where moon-worship prevails, this custom is apt to be very much exaggerated, the segregration going right through the tribe, in obedience to the supposed lunar influence on physiological conditions. This idea was at the base of the religious ceremonies in which only one sex could take part, and which we find among barbarians and even the highly civilised Greeks and Romans, but which, in the more primitive states, would cause the sexes to divide up temporarily into unisex tribes. The Amazons of Asia, we are told, were worshippers of Artemis (Astarte), who had her great mysteries only to be witnessed by women, as well as ceremonies in which both sexes mingled in secret and openly.

Fortune of war is another of those important influences which must be taken into account. With both savage and barbarian the slaying of all male prisoners is a common practice dictated by policy more than revenge, and if only the conquest is sufficiently thorough the drastic measures bring about a peculiar state of affairs. Men and women of the Carib tribe were found by the early voyagers to use different languages. The Caribs themselves explained this by saying that they were originally a mainland nation, and that they had invaded the islands and slain all the men, and after a time had married the women. This idea of conquest is also perhaps portrayed in the Maha Bharata by those incidents that we have described. Even more striking is the incident of the siege of Damascus, under Khaled, lieutenant of Abu Becker, the first Caliph, when the Moslem women were surrounded by the enemy and succeeded in beating them off. It is easy to realise that had their mankind been destroyed the plucky dames might have succeeded in securing their retreat to the hills, and there formed a "woman's tribe," which would either have endured for a brief space before melting into the surrounding population, or under stress have been artificially kept up for a generation or two. That ring of tent-pole-wielding Hamzarite women camp-followers affords a perfect example of the accidental formation of such a tribe in the making, though another turn in the fortune of war diverted the probable sequence into a happier channel.

Another phase is more than hinted at in the adventures of the Argonauts in Lemnos, as given to us by the Rhodian Apollonius. Admitting a certain amount of tribal pride and organisation among the women, it is conceivable that the male and female "nations" would be some time before effecting reconciliation and merging into one tribe. But in such cases, as in those where, as we may allow did occasionally occur, the women struggling from savagedom to barbarism went off to form their own camps or "nations," the final result was inevitable, for, as Mr. Payne says, a day comes when the women have to surrender on the men's own terms. An amusing enough illustration of this is taking place in the United States, where, some thirty years ago, a Mrs. M'Whirter, of Waco, announced that she had been inspired by the Almighty, and told to leave her husband, for it was sinful to live with man. The inspired prophetess found many willing disciples to adopt her creed, abandoning husbands, sons, fathers, brothers. So a new Women's Commonwealth sprang into being; a colony in due course was founded at Belmont, Texas, which was subsequently removed to Washington State. All went well for many years, then came a change, the eligible dames and damsels one by one forsaking their convictions; for, as one of the most recent brides candidly confessed, though "brought up in the belief that it was a sin to marry," when they met the "inevitable he" they were "just crazy over him," and thus the unnatural commonwealth breaks up to-day in America under the influence of the selfsame forces that acted thousands of years ago in Asia Minor.

As regards the alleged difference of languages used by opposite sexes, we must not attach too much importance to the matter, either in connection with the Caribs or any other people, for this state of affairs is often seen to prevail, mainly, it would almost appear, as an anti-matriarchal precaution, "superior" man having his own language for ruling and religious purposes. This is not unknown in the East, and some traces of it are to be found among the Indians of Peru. The ruling classes in all quarters of the globe often used a different language to that of the populace, and not always (as was the case with the Normans in England) as the result of conquest. The Incas had a language in which many words were secretly symbolical: thus Cuzco (or more correctly Cozco) to the ruled was merely the name of the Emperor's capital, but to the initiated it meant the umbilicus, which, having regard to the traditions of the race, was peculiarly significant—a device which has always been of immense service in welding together special castes, priestly classes, secret societies, and kindred organisations involving the observance of vows, with accompanying solidarity of interests, duties, and privileges.

Of the matriarchal stage of civilisation much might be said in this connection. It undoubtedly played a useful part, and must not be thought to have necessarily implied inferiority in the position of man. In fact, it may often be taken as evidencing the peculiarly migratory character of the male, who could not throw off his wandering habits or needs, although developing an unconscious desire for acquiring a "local habitation and a name," if not for himself at least for his offspring, and thus by the safest way in a most primitive society ensuring hereditary proprietorship in "chattels," lands, and totems. Dr. Livingstone found that among the Banyai the wives were the predominant partners, and the children of the unions belonged to the mothers' families. It was only by buying the wives (not an easy matter with them) that the children became the property of the father and his tribal section. Arrived at a certain stage on the road of evolution, such a condition, and all that it implied, would become odious to the male state, though such a feeling need not always be extended to a queen ruling over men, even of a warlike nation. There have been many strong women sovereigns, and we may take instances from one of our Amazon regions: such as the Queen of Sheba, who governed the rich and powerful country as an autocrat. That this traditional loyalty to a queen lingered in the locality we know not only from the Portuguese missionaries of the sixteenth century, but from what happened in the last century during our own

Abyssinian Expedition (1866), when the Wallo Galla country, where Magdala was and Sheba had been, was found to be ruled over by two rival and warlike queens, each with a long following of devoted male subjects.

It is not without deep meaning that while the Greeks held their warfare against the Amazons as among the most noteworthy and honourable of their feats of arms, the Indians only dreaded the odium of defeat, looking for no glory as a possible outcome of their fighting the female warriors. Yet the Greek ideal of womanhood was far inferior to that shown in early Indian traditions. The truth is, the Amazons symbolised all that was dangerous to man and State to the Greeks, something to be feared but fought and conquered; while to the Indians it meant merely a different phase of society, to be overcome rather by an intellectual revolution than by force of arms. So while the Greek fought and boasted of his successes, the Indian swept away the unnatural state by force of religious argument, and no doubt persecution. The difference shown in dealing with this troublesome matter (as it was to both) is all the more remarkable because the great Eastern Epic is not without its tales of many bloody conquests both in the military and religious fields.

Reviewing the whole subject, it seems clear that it is to religious influences that we must trace the existence of many, and probably the most startling, traditions concerning bands of women warriors and women societies. It reveals one of the most sombre sides of the human intellect. We have to go to the dark Caucasus to find the origin of the Greeks' Amazons. Here it was that Prometheus, who had stolen fire from heaven and placed divine truths at the service of mankind, was fettered to the rocks, exposed to the torture of the eagle until that bird, the emblem of priestcraft, was slain by Hercules. This was merely a symbolical presentation of what was actually taking place. For here too, as Strabo reveals, the Albanians had a sanctuary dedicated to the moon-god, a temple wherein men were sacrificed by a spear-thrust, the priests watching the fall and gush of blood for purposes of divination, after which the body was removed to a stated spot so that the people might take an active share in the sacrifice by trampling on the scapegoat and purifying themselves thereby. Farther to the north-east, at Phanagoria, near the Palus Mæotis, he also tells us, was a shrine to Venus Apatura, the Deceitful, who, having secured the aid of Hercules, allured her admirers one by one into a cave, where they were killed by the sturdy sons of Jupiter and Alcmena.

It is difficult not to see in this a local tradition with a Greek gloss, for we know how they loved to allegorise facts and to Greecise barbarian gods. Is not Venus in this instance Astarte? that Ashtoreth whom men knew as "Queen of the Heavens" and worshipped in such ghastly fashions as goddess of fertility? And is not Hercules her consort, the great Baal, giver of life and lord of fire, with his club-like thunderbolt? The whole story has the appearance of an allegorical description of some religious mysteries. By one of those peculiar, but easily understandable, workings of the human mind, worship was mainly propitiatory, linked up with the idea of sacrifice, which often led to such terrible conclusions.

Two main notions, it should be observed, underlay the theory and practice of sacrifice : the expiatory act and the propitiatory offering. In an animistic stage of development, the spirit pervaded everything. The tree-god was in the tree, the corn-god in the corn, formed part of it, and so on with the mountain, the glen, the lake, the spring, stream, and sea. Therefore, when man cut down a tree, bruised and ate corn, slew the buffalo for food, he was sacrificing the gods and had to offer thanksgiving, apology, and amends. So the flesh that was fed by the bruised corn and the slaughtered ox-god had in its turn to be bruised and slashed, hence the necessity for the ceremonial victim or the scapegoat. Then, as religion was in a sense exclusive, understood by, and concerned more directly the god-king or priest-king and the regal-priestly caste, it was for them to intercede, to offer the personal sacrifice, and later to seek for the scapegoat. While at first the god-king was himself sacrificed on the altar to the end that the people as a whole should thrive, later we find the priest-king delegating that inconvenient honour. So the king lamenting his sins, and in the agony of his contrition, caused many of his chosen people to die under the sacerdotal lash or knife, and thus by vicarious floggings or spilling of blood made atonement for his shortcoming.

To this day the transition stage is strangely exemplified in Tibet, for at Lhassa a scapegoat is annually selected from among members of the lowest caste ; he is known as the *logon gyalpo*, or " carrier of one year's ill-luck." This unhappy wretch is allowed a term of licence, during which he may go about the town doing practically as he pleases, but always carrying a yak's tail, which he waves over the heads of people to chase away evil from them and take their sins on his own head; then, amidst the ringing of bells, he is driven from the town with kicks and blows, after which he is allowed a certain time of grace, during which he may make good his escape; but he is generally so badly used that almost invariably he is overtaken and killed. What chiefly arrests our attention is the fact that the doomed man draws lots with one of the Grand Lhamas as to which of the two shall be the victim. Although, as far as man's memory runneth, there never was any doubt whatever as to the ultimate result, the formality of this mock lottery, a simulacrum of an appeal to a Power ruling the destinies of men, is pregnant with meaning, taking us back, indeed, to that exclusive form of worship of which we have written.

As one result of this exclusiveness we frequently find a strange diversity of interpretation of religious beliefs among the privileged classes and the masses. Thus we trace the most exalted spirituality among the ancient Egyptians side by side with seemingly grotesque materialistic religious observances. Among the black savages and the copper-coloured barbarians we have evidence of lofty ideals of a Supreme Creator and of a Heavenly Hereafter, understood but by the elect of the ruling and priestly castes, while to the people religion is often of the grossest character. We see this in its most degraded form as recorded by John Cartwright of the Kurds, who "do adore and worship the devil, to the end that he may not hurt them or their cattle," or, as Father Bouché writes of the West African, whose devotion to his fetish (the native *oricha*: "he who sees" or "listens to" prayers) is defended by the black man on the ground that the Beneficent Creator is very far off, but the demons too near at home, with power to do harm. Under such conditions the propitiatory sacrifice is the rule. Either the offended god has to be appeased, or more often the evil spirit put into a good temper by an offering. As the tree puts forth branches, the seed begets the waving corn and its grain crop, so to ensure prosperity —which in its essential meant multiplication, fertility— life, or its equivalent, had to be given up. Hence the hanging of victims to trees; the fettering of them to mountains to be pierced by the darts of the sun and the fire from the clouds and eaten by those aerial Mercuries, the vultures and eagles; the casting of sacrifices into rivers that crop-fattening floods might follow, or into the sea to the end that fish might be plentiful and the elements kind; the spilling of human blood in temples; the anointing of living bodies or sticks or stones; and the mutilations and renuncitions of various kinds and in differing degrees.

The Hindu carries this theory of penance so far that the mere repetition of prayers, ceremonial observances, accompanied by sacrifices, no matter by whom undertaken or for what purpose, gained an irresistible power for the persevering ascetic over heaven and earth, gods and demons. Not only holy men, but gods and, on the other hand, evil necromancers obtained such dominion by penance. Which unites them on the one side with the Egyptians and their theory in the efficacy of the sacred books as talismans and of the use of the mystic "Words of Power," on the other with the magicians and their "Abracadabra" and formularies. But, if we only go back far enough, we find that these "Words of Power" of any kind can only be secured by deeds of austerity, in the form either of personal penance or vicarious atonement, and propitiatory offerings of sacrifices. Herodotus says that the Egyptians beat themselves after offering sacrifices to Isis; but Strabo tells us of far more significant human sacrifice in the Caucasus, and darkly reveals two other forms at Phanagoria; for we know that both death and even more terrible kinds of self-sacrifice were offered to Astarte and to Baal. A point of which we are bound to take note is raised by Mr. J. G. Frazer, who suggests that Astarte became a moon goddess as the result of an error, or rather a confusion in art representation. He points out that in the Semitic language the moon is masculine, and says that it is through the very early influence of Egyptian art in Assyria that the moon was associated with the Eastern goddess. Both Isis and Hathor are sun goddesses, usually depicted as adorned with the sun disc between two cows' horns placed on their heads. Often the horns are shown alone, and this may have given rise to the notion that the disc was the full moon and the horns the crescent moon. So, he holds, Astarte was given the horns of the crescent moon. While giving this all due weight, we must not forget that Astarte and her congeners were the consorts of Baal and his congeners, and regarded as the goddess of the night sky. The peculiar appearance of the moon in its last phase, with the darkened disc seemingly resting in the bright crescent cup; its total disappearance, to be followed by a reappearance of a small curved fillet

ARMED WOMEN, WITH THE KING AT THEIR HEAD, GOING TO WAR.

Facing page 193.]

which gradually grew, led to its being regarded as feminine, as abundant folklore testifies.

The Babylonian trinity consisted of Anu, the Creator; Sin, the sun god; and Ishtar, the moon goddess, who wore the crescent. As the planet was credited with influence on fertility generally, we have one reason for certain specialised sacrificial ceremonies connected with the worship of that goddess in her many manifestations, from the grim Ishtar to the more gentle, though often cruel, Venus. Some hint of this we have in relation to the Amazons of the Caucasus, who, according to Strabo, spent two months of each spring on a neighbouring mountain which formed the boundary between their own territory and that of the Gargarenses, who also ascended the mountain, so that, in obedience to ancient custom, they might perform common sacrifices. They met "in secret and in darkness," as might be expected from worshippers of Astarte. Evidence of other forms of self-sacrifice seem to be referred to in the legends of the American Amazons, *e.g.* (1) those who, in order to obtain the fertility talismans, had to wound their own bodies and offer their blood; (2) the whole Amazon tribe disappearing in a hole in the earth, led by an armadillo. Again, we have the tale of the infant placed in a bag and squeezed into a new and beautiful shape. As de Gubernatis has shown, the sack has two symbolical meanings: it is the night, or the clouds hiding the sun—therefore death; and it also denotes the act of devouring, another form of death. But night and death, though a conflict with the sun and light, are merely means to renewed life. The American Amazon sacrifices her boy so that he may have a beautiful rebirth, and, as we know, the saintly youth goes through a second form of sacrifice, being thrown into the lake and metamorphosed into a fish, that other symbol of life-giving power, and as such is worshipped by the women and finally again sacrificed. This sacrifice, it will be remembered, was effected by means of entanglement in a net woven from the hair of women. Now, in many places the worship of the moon goddess entailed abandonment of the female body within the dark temples to all strangers who might come, or in lieu thereof the milder offering of their tresses.

We are told in the Maha Bharata that Shantanu, descendant of Chandra, the great moon god of Northern India, married the incarnated Ganges. This beneficent river goddess had assumed human shape as a penance, probably in order to obtain greater power, and on her earthly pilgrimage she had met seven minor gods, who told her a most piteous tale. By an unlucky chance, these mystic seven had come between a holy hermit and his sacrifice, and he, being a man with enormous accumulated power as the result of long-continued acts of austerity, had, with the usual irascibility of the self-righteous, cursed them with the terrible doom: "Be born among men." So Ganges, taking pity on them, married Shantanu, and the seven sons of the royal and divine pair were the seven gods. As each was born, his earthly destiny having thus been fulfilled, she threw him into the mighty stream, whence he straightway entered heaven.

Here, it would seem, is a clear allusion to offers of human sacrifices to the fertilising goddess-river.

It corresponds with what we know of the great Nile Sed ceremonials of the Egyptian flood time. Greatly modified, we find it again in the marriage of the Doge of Venice with the Adriatic, the Doge casting into the waves a symbolical ring that he might gain dominion over them; and yet again in the blessing of the waters, whether it be by priests in the Mediterranean or by czars on the Neva; or again by the offerings freely given by fishermen, which may take the form of the silver coin placed by Yorkshire boatmen in the corks of their nets, or the casting of the Adonis gardens into the waves by Sicilians and others. All these are sacrifices meant to repay the rivers (or the sea) for their gifts of food and prosperity to the people, sacrifices which in the case of the Ganges were afterwards softened into the custom of throwing the dead, or their ashes, into the sacred waters, so that they might be born again into a higher sphere, and in that of the Nile by the substitution of flowers for the maidens.

Herodotus has a curious story about the Libyan Auseans, who dwelt on the shores of Lake Titonis. Their maidens once a year held a feast in honour of Minerva. This we may take to be Neith or Nit,—that is, Night,—whom the Egyptians regarded as one of the trio of primitive gods, as the Mother, Nature, or in some sense the First Principle, and whom they depicted as a nude black female, arched over, resting on finger-tips and toes, bespangled with stars to represent the vault of heaven. At these celebrations it was the custom for the girls "to draw up in two bodies and to fight with staves and clubs." The loveliest maiden was clad in armour, of Greek design in the days of the chronicler, who wonders, but cannot guess, what manner of defensive gear they had worn before they came into contact with the Hellenes. Those of the girls who fell in the fight were declared to be "false maidens." Herodotus goes on to say that the Auseans held that Minerva (Neith) was the daughter of Neptune and Lake Titonis, and was adopted by Jupiter. The whole of this is suggestive of religious celebrations carrying out the idea of conflict between two elements or powers, good and evil, with the underlying notion of the benefits to be derived from sacrifice. The Ausean genesis of Neith is a tale of opposing influences, some life phenomena observed as the outcome of the blending of salt and fresh water under the action of the sun. It was appropriate enough that the ceremonies connected with the birth of the grim primitive Neith should be an affair of the armed guard of maidens and associated with strife between light and darkness, the triumph of the true devotees and the slaying of the false.

In another quarter Father Lamberti records that a tribe in the northern parts of the Caucasus, living in elevated fortified villages, did not bury their dead, but placed their bodies in hollow trees, and hung the deceased's clothing on the branches. Now, both the Asiatic Adonis and the Egyptian Osiris were originally tree gods, and their bodies were concealed in trees, so that it came about that human sacrifices were hung on trees. We find allusion to this custom in the Maha Bharata, where we are told that the Aswamedha horse led Rajah Arjuna to a land wherein men and women grew on trees, hanging therefrom, flourishing for a day and then dying. The same story occurs in connection with the women's island of El-Wak-Wak, the fruits crying out "Wak-wak" when they were ripe and then dying. Burton suggests that these trees were the calabash, "that grotesque growth, a vegetable elephant, whose gourds, something larger than a man's head, hang by a slender filament." This fruit of the calabash or baobab, the "monkey bread," contains an acid pulp which plays no insignificant part in the matter of provisioning; so here, as with the pine tree of Adonis and the palm of Osiris, and possibly the oak of the Caucasus, all food trees, we have an explanation of the arboreal hangings. It is at the base of the whole philosophy of the widespread worship of the Tree of Life—often the Tree of Death, death being the preliminary of renewed life.

Something of this necessity for sacrifice we find, too, in connection with the ancient religious observances of India, as we have been reminded by our notes on the Arddhanarishwara of the Caves of Elephanta. Both Shiva and Parvati are mountain-born and associated with human sacrifice—he actively, she passively. Shiva, "he of whom increase is," is the "Lord of the Mountains," whose seat is Mount Kailasa and whose haunts are the Himalayas, those grim ranges which the ancients regarded as the easternmost spur of the Caucasus, and which brought forth his consort, Parvati, "Daughter of the Mountains." He is a modified reincarnation of the hoary Vedic Rudra, "God of Storms," and although his emblems are the crescent moon of increase and the trident form of the fertilising thunderbolt, yet he also wears the deadly cobra and is decked with collars of snakes and human skulls.

Vestiges of human sacrifices are still extant in the seclusion of the Himalayas and other Indian mountain chains. For instance, among the Todas of the Nilgiris, where certain sacred herds migrate from one dairy to another, the Kaltmuk, or boy attendant, or acolyte, is fed with rich food when he reaches the new dairy (which corresponds to the term of licence accorded to the Tibetan *logon gyalpo*, and to other graces extended to scapegoats), and then, being led forth by the priest-dairyman, is heaped with curses, so that all ill-luck threatening the cattle, dairy, or priests may be transferred to his shoulders. This done, with many ceremonial formalities clarified butter is poured on the boy's head, and he is left alone. The priests return to the dairy: so does the boy, but at leisure, and he has to pass part of the night outside the hut, creeping in when all are asleep, and slipping out again before break of day. No one pays any attention to him until the morning's work is over, for he is not supposed to exist; then the priests go through a form of ritual for the removal of the curses from his head, and so the Kaltmuk is free to return to his duties.

But there can be little doubt that this second ceremonial is an innovation; originally the boy did not return after the sundown anointing. In other cases, it is over certain stones away from the dairies that either butter-milk or clarified butter is poured, and we may conjecture that these were altars for human sacrifices, as the anointing is never observed when calves or bullocks are sacrificed either for purposes of augury or as offerings to the ghosts of the departed. Ghee was commonly poured over sacrificial victims, and ancient Indian religious books tell us that the vampire snake-worshipping women and other magicians of the forests anointed their own bodies with the fat of victims when they began their incantations. The same thing, we have seen, occurred in the Congo, in connection with Voodooism, and probably occurred in the Andes. As for Shiva, while he wields that life symbol the trident, and that other the cobra, he also grasps the *pasha*, or sacrificial noose, with which victims were strangled, and of which certain sects made such ghastly use, approximating to the practices of the Amur Tatars and the women royal guards of the White Nile.

Of the Amazons' part in such practices as these we have much other evidence. As we have already remarked, in early stages of civilisation the king is usually a god-king, and later a priest-king. It was a high office, but, as we have seen, one often fraught with awful consequences; for the divine ruler passed to the other world self-immolated, or by the assistance of his priestly attendants, who often were women. Thus we see the Behr king on the White Nile surrounded by a female guard, strangled when on his death-bed. This form of "happy dispatch" for honoured persons was widely prevalent. It still survives in a degraded form among the "Fish-Skinned" Tatars of the Amur. These degenerate nomads, who live on fish and dress in fish skins, habitually strangle their old folk with certain suggestive ritual. Drums are beaten, and all persons leave the camp except the victim and two near relatives, who act as executioners, or rather sacrificers. The grim work is carried out in the tent while the drums are being beaten outside. That women guards took part in such ceremonial death-scenes has been shown, and their semi-sacerdotal office is evident in many ways. Snelgrave reports that in his day the King of Dahomey, though not secluded, yet kept aloof from his people and even his courtiers. His chiefs and others during audiences, having prostrated themselves and kissed the ground, whispered whatever they wished to reach the royal ears into those of an old woman, who went to the king, transmitted the message, and then returned with the answer. Which shows another stage in the intervention of the privileged councillor between the sacred person and the supplicant. Then, as we know, the petty King of Abeokuta, also on the west coast of Africa, was guarded by women, while in the same region the King of Yoruba formerly possessed a female guard, and the executioner "wives" of the King of Wydah were 5000 in number.

Turning in another direction, we find the same thing presenting itself at Pataliputra in the Punjab, and we hear of Indian rajahs going out hunting surrounded by armed female warriors, corresponding in this particular with the King of Dahomey and his picked Elephant Huntresses. In Bantam it appears to have been the custom for the women royal guards to elect from among their own sons a new king in default of a direct heir. All this we may compare to Megasthenes' account, who says that the women guards at Pataliputra were at liberty to kill the king if found drunk, the executioner marrying the successor.

Throughout all this we may note differences of detail, but the mission of these women as a buffer class between the claimant to superhuman attributes and his people is clear enough. How illuminating, therefore, to find this phenomenon of organising a special guard of women repeating itself in Eastern China in the fifth and sixth decades of the nineteenth century, as though spontaneously evolved from the exigencies of the case. When those misnamed "Princes of Peace," the Tae-pings, inaugurated a vast religious movement, they declared that they were expecting a sacred leader. To them appeared that "Celestial Virtue," Tien-wang, and, claiming both divinity in his own person as second son of God and dominion over the world as regent of the Celestial King, it seemed to follow naturally that he should be protected by a bodyguard of women warriors. And although the religious movement quickly assumed a political phase, the fanatical aspect only increased as the Celestial King and his female guard swept through the land, carrying fire and sword in every direction in the name of peace and goodwill.

It is remarkable that the ancients in writing of the African Amazons, and American Indian traditions, describe the warrior women as a "white" race. It has been argued from this that both the African and American Amazons must have been emigrants from Europe or Asia. But assuming that there was foundation for the reports, the fact would be capable of quite another interpretation. It would point, indeed, to an exclusive class. As Sir Richard

Burton rightly says, though in a different connection: "Rank makes some difference in colour; the higher it is the fairer the skin. . . . Even amongst the negroes of Central Africa we find the chief lighter-tinted than his subjects." To the black or copper-coloured a slight lessening in shade means "white." Tradition, therefore, seems to indicate, at all events in the earlier stages, the existence of an exclusive caste of warrior women both in Africa and America, and with some associated idea of self-sacrifice. They were, like the Lenâpé "Woman" tribe of North America, and the mutilated beings of Central and South Africa, as well as of Asia Minor in ancient times, somewhat in the position of scapegoats.

Captain John Adams, writing about the Congo (in 1823), says: "One of the conditions by which a female is admitted into the order of priesthood is leading a life of celibacy and renouncing the pleasures of the world." This renunciation was certainly the prevalent idea as regards the Dahomeyan Amazons in the early days, and perhaps also, so far as regards the queen, in the regions of the White Nile. At least one of the Portuguese missionaries declares that the queen of the Abyssinian Amazons was looked up to by her neighbours as a goddess, and the same was said of the mysterious foundress of that equally mysterious second great will-o'-the-wisp golden city of the continent, Dobayba, about which Vasca Nuñez de Balboa and his successors on the Isthmus of Darien heard so much and dared many perils in vain to seek. Certain legends said that Dobayba was a mighty female who lived at the beginning of time, mother of the god who created the sun, moon, and all things—in fact, the supreme Nature goddess. Others asserted that she was a powerful Indian princess who had held sway among the mountains, built a beautiful city, enriched with gold, and gained widespread renown for her wisdom and military prowess. After her death she was regarded as a divinity and worshipped in a golden temple. Traditions were persistent of a rich concealed temple, where neighbouring caciques and their subjects made pilgrimage, carrying offerings of gold and slaves to be sacrificed. Neglect of these rites brought drought, most dreaded of Nature's punishments. Farther south we hear much the same tale of the Brazilian warrior women (who were "whiter than other women") in Nuño de Gusman's letter to the Emperor Charles v.

Nevertheless, the vestal state is by no means essential to the religious idea. Angelo Mosso, writing of the Minoan age in Crete, finely says: "Priestesses were mothers and maidens who initiated the Greek race into the religion of beauty." That, however, was in an advanced stage. Often the sacerdotal state might, indeed, enjoin abstention from marriage, yet demand personal sacrifice. This was unquestionably the case with the followers of Astarte. There appears to be a hint of that state of affairs in the curious traditions recorded by Strabo which we have already cited, and again in the legend of the American Amazons, who took to the hill caves with only one old man, to whom they ministered. The "marriage" to the King of Dahomey, and at Wydah, would have a ceremonial import if we regard these monarchs as priest-(descendants of tribal god-) kings. And in this connection we may take note of Sir Richard Burton's description of the eighteen Tansi-no, or fetish women, of Dahomey, who had charge of the king's grave. These women, who were accompanied by a band playing on horns and rattles (always and everywhere associated with magic and incantations), were called the "King's Ghosts," and were said to be of the blood royal. These were the terrestrial counterparts of the sacrificed female retinue who accompanied the dead king into the grave. The mere fact that the Dahomeyan dynasty was a modern one does not invalidate such arguments, for the kings and the people were inheritors of the immemorial customs. Another interesting point is that these black Amazons, when they took their walks abroad, were always preceded by a small girl ringing a bell, so that common mortals should make way for the privileged women, reminding us irresistibly of the vestal processions in classic times. Nor must we forget that tradition said the Amazons from the Thermodon dwelt within the sanctuary at Ephesus. Pausanias makes distinct mention of this, though he contradicts the story that the sanctuary had actually been founded by them. Putting aside all question of Themysciran Amazons, it would seem from this statement quite clear that some of the priestesses and female attendants must have had a reputation for more or less martial qualities: they were at once the ministrants and the guards. That Artemis herself still retained her Eastern reputation as a warrior appears not improbable when we consider that at Aulis in Attica there were two statues to her, one in the guise of a huntress, while in the other she was represented as grasping two torches, which symbolised not the holding aloft of the pure flame of the nobler passions (generally represented by a single torch), but the brandishing of war signals.

Two matters may be touched upon lightly: the association of the Amazons with sun and moon worship and with cannibalism. Strabo is our authority for the sanctuary to the moon god in the Caucasus and the shrine to Venus Apatura, while we know the Greeks all declared the Amazons worshipped Artemis (Astarte) and carried crescent-shaped shields. In Africa such records as we have connect the women warriors with the sun god, as evidenced by their use of snake skins, alligator and tortoise emblems, and their alliance with Horus; but Ptolemy refers to the Moon Mountain in Central Africa, apparently in the regions where the Abyssinian and White Nile Amazons were placed. In America we find the association with moon-worship both through the legends and the greenstone fertility amulets. In the mountains of the upper reaches of the Amazon River, however, we find great peaks crowned by temples bearing symbols both of the sun and moon, and other mountains called the Mansion of the Sun, the Seat of the Sun, and so on.

The connection with cannibalism is rather more vague except in so far as it concerns the Far East. Certain Greek writers say that the Amazons of the Thermodon drank out of human skulls, and many of the Asiatic legends refer to the dwellers in female colonies as eaters of men. But this expression of "eaters of men" may generally be taken as a figure of speech, on the one hand paying a doubtful tribute to women's wiles, and on the other referring picturesquely to their fighting powers. An army that carries all before it "eats up" the enemy, just like a cloud of locusts. In this sense, to "eat up" men is to slay, to wipe out, although it must be allowed that the figurative may originally have been truly descriptive. This is undoubtedly the case so far as Africa is concerned. The usual Greek qualifying epithet applied to the women was the milder "slayer of men." The Eastern legends—those related of Ceylon, of the great Indian forests, and of the imaginary El-Wak-Wak—clearly allude to anthropophagy as a habitual practice of the women. We have trace of this in at least one of the American tales, where we are told of a mother placing her sick boy in a bag and crushing him into a beautiful shape, which is suggestive of something more than ordinary human sacrifice, for placing in a bag is often a synonym for "devouring." Cannibalism existed in all this part of the continent, nay, still persists there, while one tribe possesses the remarkable habit and secret of removing bones from corpses and then dwarfing and desiccating them. There are traditions, too, in the Andes of human sacrifices for the purpose of ceremonial anointings, a practice which must have been in force prior to the days of the Incas, for we are told that this mysterious race was opposed to all such customs. It must be remembered that cannibalism had a religious import, though it may have originated in various parts of the world from motives of economic pressure. It was not, however, always a matter of satisfying appetite, the cravings of a depraved habit, or even an exhibition of revenge;

there was the idea that by eating the enemy his strength was incorporated, and even the dead man's ghost enlisted as a kind of secondary guardian spirit. For the same reason the skulls of enemies were kept, and placed high on poles, above huts, and so on, as Herodotus reports of the savage Tauri, and even fed, as by the "Head Hunters" of Borneo, who stuck cheroots between the parched lips to keep these ghastly guardians in good humour.

As a rule, however, the armed Amazons seemed to be ranged against cannibalism. In Greek tradition the Amazons not only fought and overcame the man-eating gryphons, but, according to some, helped Hercules in his struggles with the Hydra, and farther back assisted Dionysus against the giants. As to the early African Amazons, we also see them waging war against the savage black races, who, on the testimony of even late Arabic authors, we know, "ate men"; and this warfare was carried on, Pigafetta tells us, by the Congo Amazons and the giant anthropophagists down to the end of the sixteenth century.

It is curious to find that where rumours of fighting Amazons are most persistent we have abundant proof of primitive savagery lingering on. The fabulous Isle of the East, inhabited by women, where human sacrifices prevailed, was called El-Wak-Wak because "Wak-wak" was the only word uttered by the ceremonial victims. The Western African women, in their endeavours to reach Egypt, had to pass through a land peopled by cannibal tribes bearing the repeat names Nem-Nems, Gnem-Gnems, the Niam-Niams of to-day, who call their neighbours the

Akka Tikki-Tikki.[1] In the Amazon valley and the Andes such duplication is common as regards topographical names—for instance, the Huari-huari and Pina-pina rivers, Lake Titikaka; the mountain Sara-sara; Chapi-chapi village; and there is also the Inje-inje tribe, who are extremely retiring forest folk, still in the stone age of development, and are supposed to use only the one word "inje" doubled, with different inflexions to express all their wants and feelings, in this resembling the tree-grown puellæ Wakwakiensis. This repetition in all kinds of ways is a favourite form of emphasis with primitive people, just as it is with small children.

In passing, we may note the fact that in the three great centres of Amazonian traditions—in Asia, Africa, and America—though we have mention of mountains and forests, the real seats of activity are on extensive alluvial plains. Such situations have always been cradles of new nations and of social revolutions, for it is in these rich granaries that peoples mingle, man multiplies, where interests clash, giving rise to upheavals and abnormalities, until a new order of affairs has been evolved.

That there was some justification for the legends there can be no reasonable doubt. The very diversity met with in regard to them is strongly in favour of some solid foundation having existed; because, if we consider them critically, they answer to some need of humanity. If we take into account the tendency,

[1] According to Arab traditions, Gian ben Gian was the gigantic king of the Jinns, founder of the pyramids, who, having rebelled against God, was defeated by Lucifer before his fall. The Jinns then became mischievous spirits of the dark and of lonely places.

PUBLIC PROCESSION OF THE KING'S WOMEN, ETC.

Facing page 208.]

on the one hand, to exaggerate, and on the other the frailty of mankind in the matter of giving and receiving evidence, we have much still left. We know that the Greeks loved the declamatory form; the Orientals revel in the superlative. We have seen the pitfalls that beset the inquiring explorers in America, and we have a similar note of warning from West Africa, where Father Bouché says: "Native interpreters aim less at being very accurate than at not displeasing the white man. They do not fail to flatter him by giving translations which they know he desires, or rather which they are aware will fall in with his views."

Even apart from what we may be permitted to call these amenities of the "traitrous translators'" art, mistakes may arise innocently enough from sheer confusion of tongues, a blundering all too easy in matters both great and small, as daily experience sufficiently demonstrates. Take as an instance a little incident that came under the writer's own observation. A very small boy was in the habit of calling a particularly favoured lady of his acquaintance his "clean friend," to her immense delight but to the scandalised bewilderment of the child's parents. Then it was discovered that the youngster had been translating Italian into English through the medium of French. "Propria" became "propre," and, of course, "propre" meant "clean," therefore "il mia propria amica" ("mine own particular friend") became his "clean friend." Assuredly perfectly logical, and not without a certain poetical symbolism of speech all the more pleasing for its very spontaneous unconscious cerebration, yet which, under different circumstances, might have proved grotesquely misleading. We are all—savages, barbarians, and civilised—little children in this transmutation of thought into concrete phrase, with the help of all too unstable words and the evasive flux of grammatical rules. Yet admitting all this, and allowing it to have due weight in its application to our particular study, we may conclude that the legends should be credited to a large extent.

Let us clearly bear in mind our original three divisions of the subject. Of the third we need say little, for the matriarchal stage of civilisation has to be accepted in many quarters; and of great and little nations governed by women who not seldom were great fighters before the Lord, history repeatedly attests. We will only allude to this as a possible source of confusion, the outstanding deeds of a queen and her women captains being tacked on to or mixed up with the traditions of some more or less transitory women's camp. Into this category the Damute Amazons evidently, and the Bohemian Valasca probably, fall.

We have, then, the two first divisions. That, through the exigencies of social organisation, women and young children had, and still have in a minor degree, to live alone periodically and for many months on end, is proved by actual experience. Local conditions may have occasionally emphasised this peculiarity, which would easily be evolved into a theory of an autonomous female community. It may be conceded that these conditions, combined with a rebellion against male tyranny under the stress of struggling from savagedom to higher things, may frequently have led to revolts and temporary pacts among women, who lived apart and only admitted men as an act of toleration or policy. Such "nations" and "tribes" were probably enough also brought about as the result of conquest, the conquerors having slain all males, and, for a time, which would vary according to local social progress and especially topographical peculiarities, failed to subdue the females. Where there were mountains difficult of access, or dense forests, probably with swamp-isolated islands, no doubt the women with their children would preserve their savage aloofness all the longer, and would, having almost certainly a previous acquaintance with warfare, be able to give a very good account of themselves as warriors, whether acting purely on the defensive or actively retaliating on the enemy. Under these circumstances, communication between the sexes would arise only gradually, and be of a spasmodic, even of a clandestine nature, until the inevitable day came when the women surrendered to the men on the latter's own terms; for such is the predestined fate of all such "commonwealths," ancient or modern. But, given a mountainous country, or a district covered by primeval forest, and obstinate resistance, the women tribe would soon be regarded as something outside of nature, either to be cursed or fought, and almost certainly to be looked upon with a mixture of dread and veneration.

This brings us to the fighting organisation. Now, both the temporary colonies of women evolved by natural everyday causes, and those feminine camps brought about by an abnormal concatenation of circumstances, would obviously have to organise for defence in savage and barbaric stages of evolution; and where the women had been accustomed to aid and abet their men in warfare, which is generally the case among nomadic tribes and mountaineers or forest dwellers, this organisation might be carried very far indeed. There were, then, we may conclude, women banded together to defend their homes, and others who joined the ranks, or even led men in warfare. But the fighting organisations as such were not the outcome of unisex "nations," they belong to the domain of religion. The god-king would have his armed guard, and these, we have seen, were often armed women, either because of the form of the worship or because of their fierceness, and such guards were, at all events in the earlier periods, a sacrificial body; and then the priest-king would strengthen his guards, converting them from his jailers, or perhaps more correctly from those who assisted him in his personal self-immolation, into ministrants of his own personal cult and policy, as exemplified by the King of Wydah and his thousands of "wives" who executed the royal sentences. When such guards grew numerous, it must often have become a matter of convenience and expediency to assign them special quarters, or even provinces, thus forming the nations, as we are told was the case in the Congo, and seems probable in connection with some of the sanctuaries in the Caucasus and Asia Minor. In such cases the women warriors would naturally come in time to form castes—or perhaps we had better say a privileged circle within the nation—and not a "nation" by themselves. They formed part of the social economy, and were not outside of it, though they might appear to be so when coming into contact with other races. And so we shall conclude by rejecting the idea of a long-sustained women's state, or even tribe (allowing for the exception of a transitory accident), while accepting the "women's islands" in a modified form, and the fighting Amazons as religious, or regal-religious, bodies.

Even thus stripped of much of the marvellous, the problem is intensely interesting. While teaching us the fundamental unity of nature, manifested not less in the tendency to fall into error and distort half-truths until they degenerate so far as to seemingly sanction ghastly practices, than in its aspirations to higher things, it happily points to the immense strides accomplished in the march of progress. Onrushing waves necessarily involve the disconcerting phenomena of reflux eddies, which seem to tell of the elusive nature of hope, so that we are often cast down as we reflect on present conditions and contrast them with the near past, mellowed as such views are into a haunting beauty by the glamour of blurring sentiment. Nevertheless, if our retrospective glance is sufficiently comprehensive, the evidence of secured progress is unmistakable, and so we are heartened to look forward to a bright future that assuredly will not be ours, but to which humanity is heir, and whose advent we may all in some measure contribute to hasten.

INDEX